MATHEMATICS

Grade K • Student Edition

Second Edition

purposeful design
p u b l i c a t i o n s

Colorado Springs, Colorado

© 2004, 2015 by ACSI/Purposeful Design Publications
All rights reserved. First edition 2004.
Second edition 2015

Printed in the United States of America
26 25 24 23 22 21 20   3 4 5 6 7 8 9

Mathematics, Kindergarten – Student Edition
Purposeful Design Mathematics series
ISBN 978-1-58331-575-0, Catalog #400K1

Purposeful Design Publications is the publishing division of the Association of Christian Schools International (ACSI) and is committed to the ministry of Christian school education, to enable Christian educators and schools worldwide to effectively prepare students for life. As the publisher of textbooks, trade books, and other educational resources within ACSI, Purposeful Design Publications strives to produce biblically sound materials that reflect Christian scholarship and stewardship and that address the identified needs of Christian schools around the world.

References to books, computer software, and other ancillary resources in this series are not endorsements by ACSI. These materials were selected to provide teachers with additional resources appropriate to the concepts being taught and to promote student understanding and enjoyment.

Purposeful Design Publications
A Division of ACSI
731 Chapel Hills Drive • Colorado Springs, CO 80920
Customer Service Department: 800-367-0798
Website: www.purposefuldesign.com

Table of Contents

Chapter 13 Measurement

Chapter 1
Classify and Sort

I have no greater joy than to hear that my children are walking in the truth.
3 John 4

Key Ideas:

Patterns: identifying attributes

Patterns: sorting objects into two groups

Patterns: identifying attributes that distinguish a set

Patterns: identifying objects that do not belong in a set

Use the Key to color.

Key

Name _____

Draw a ball on the middle shelf and a toy on the top shelf.

top

middle

bottom

Circle the item in each stack.

 top

 middle

 middle

 bottom

Name _____

Listen and draw.

stripes

carrot

branch

whiskers

Draw yourself in each position.

 after

 before

 between

Draw.

above

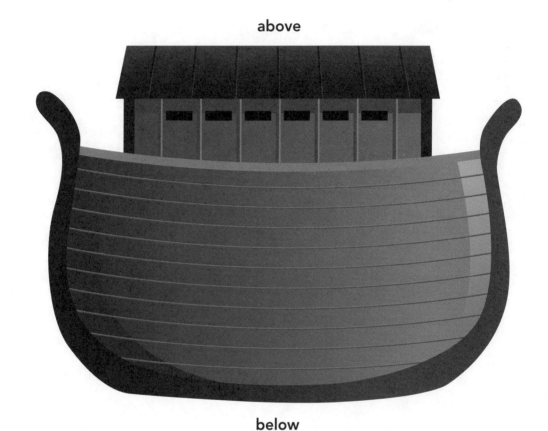

below

Cut and glue the pictures.

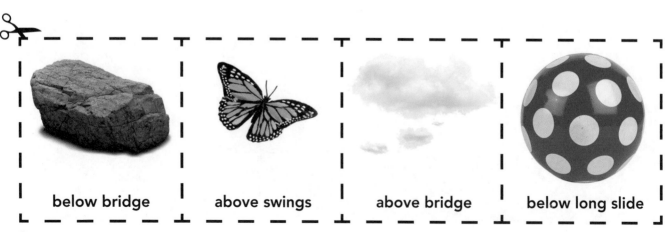

| below bridge | above swings | above bridge | below long slide |

Left and Right 1.4

Trace the hands.

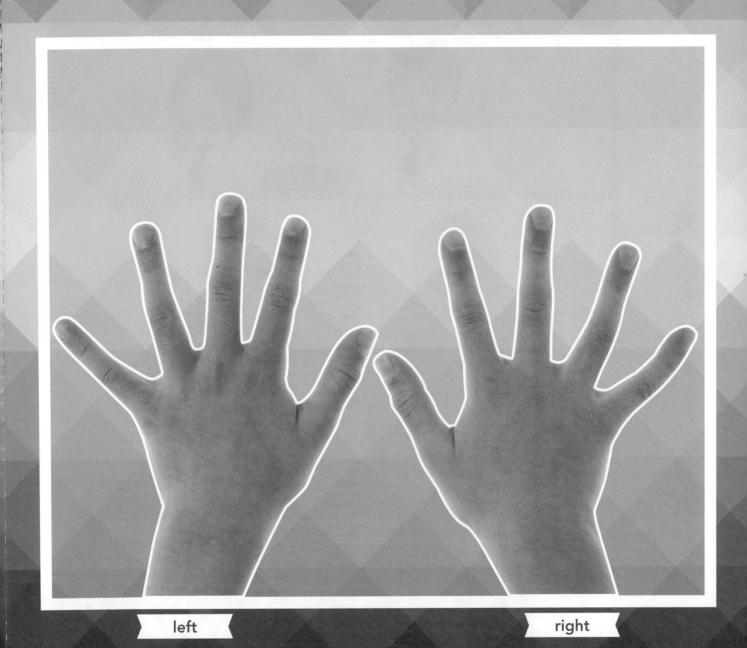

left   right

Circle the child.

⭐ right

⭐ left

⭐ right

Inside and Outside 1.5

What goes inside? Draw lines.

Circle.

inside

outside

inside

outside

Name _____

Circle each color group.

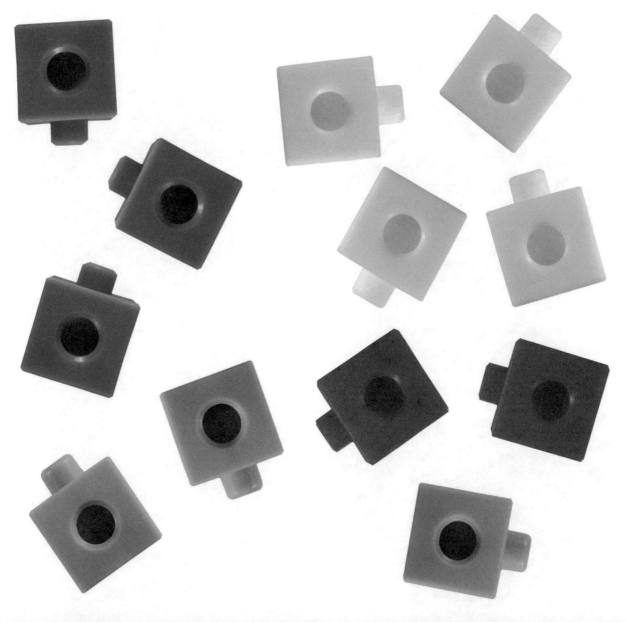

Cut and glue to match colors.

Name _____

Use the Key to color.

Mark an X on the shapes.

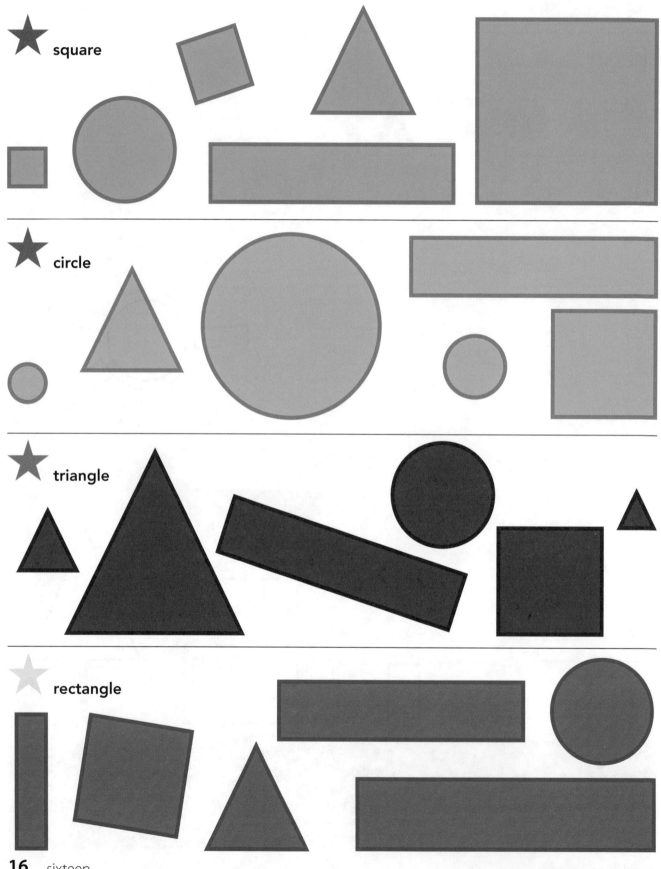

★ square

★ circle

★ triangle

★ rectangle

Circle the two groups by size.

Draw a line to match the items by size. Color each group of large items.

Circle two that are alike.

Mark an X on one that is different.

Name _____

Color. Circle the largest group.

Cut and glue the pictures to the graph.

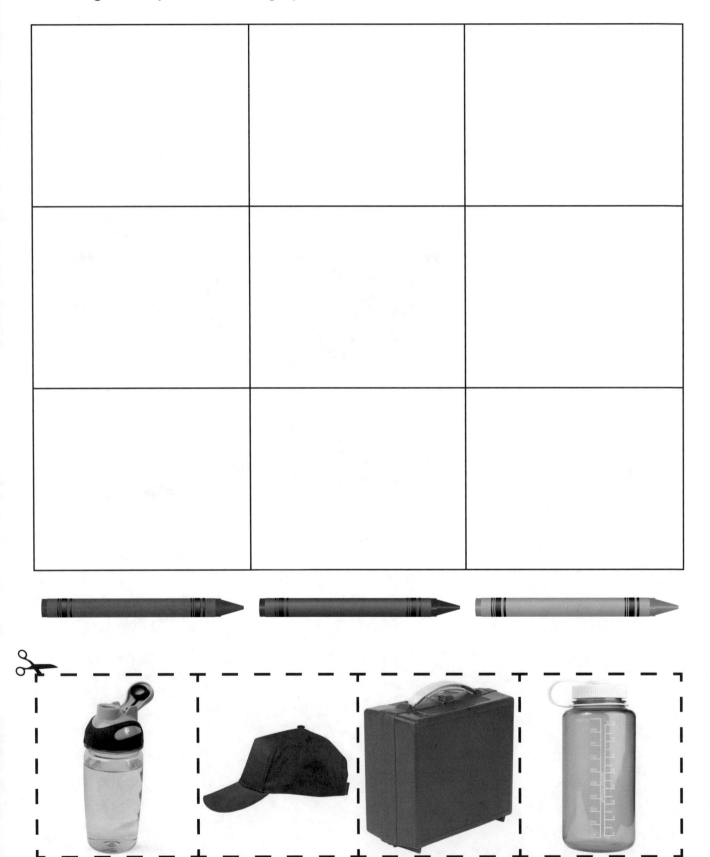

Circle.

★ top

★ inside

★ right

★ alike

Draw items that match the key words.

 squares

 little marbles

 a bee above

 a car after

Name _____

Circle.

⭐ left

⭐ different

⭐ middle

⭐ outside

Mark an X.

⭐ squares

⭐ big

⭐ below

⭐ between

Chapter 2
Explore Patterns

See how the farmer waits for the land to yield its valuable crop, patiently waiting for the autumn and spring rains.
James 5:7b

Key Ideas:

Patterns: identifying patterns

Patterns: copying a given pattern

Patterns: describing a pattern

Patterns: identifying the next object in a pattern

Color.

Name _____

Color the patterns to match.

⭐

⭐

Color the patterns.

⭐

⭐

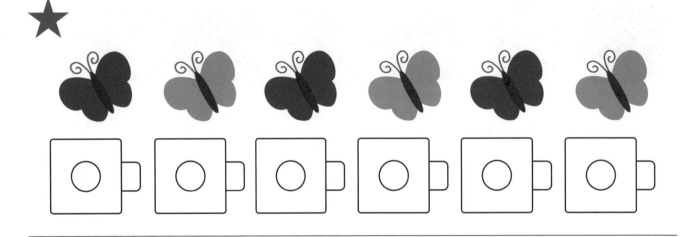

⭐

Trace the patterns. Listen and color.

Circle the matching pattern.

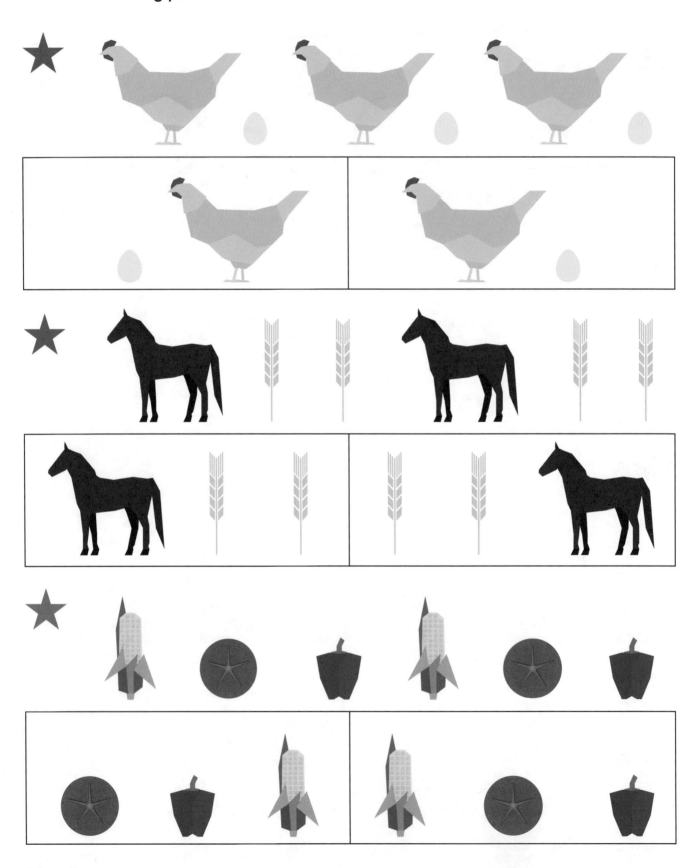

Cut and glue the pattern.

Circle what comes next.

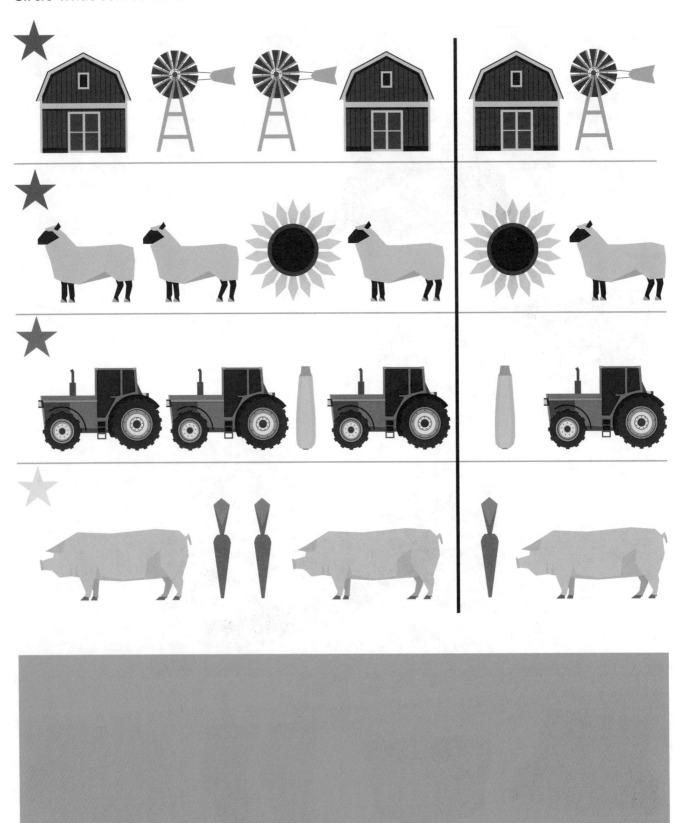

Cut and glue the pattern pieces.

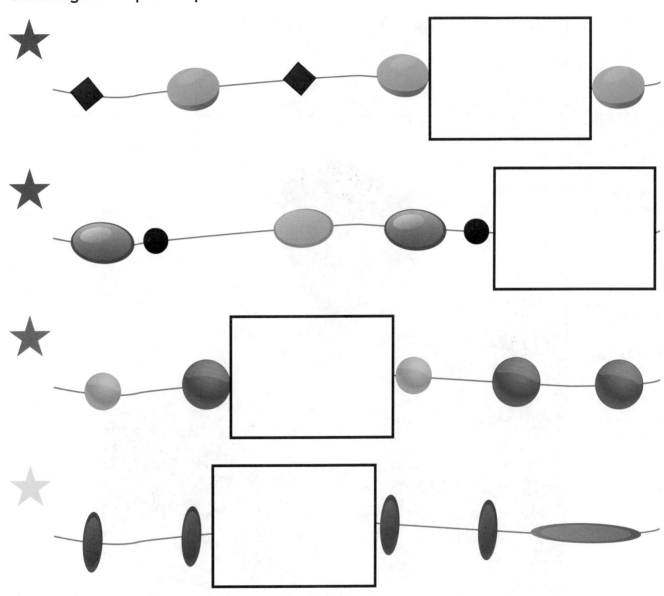

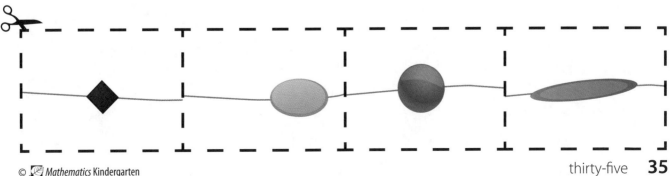

Color the border to complete the pattern.

Name _____

Circle the patterns that are alike.

Draw lines to match the patterns to the letters.

.AAB

.AB

.ABB

Circle the letters that match the pattern.

AB   AAB   ABB

Circle the repeated patterns.

Color and draw the ABC patterns.

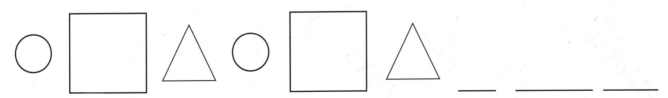

Color and write the letter to make the pattern.

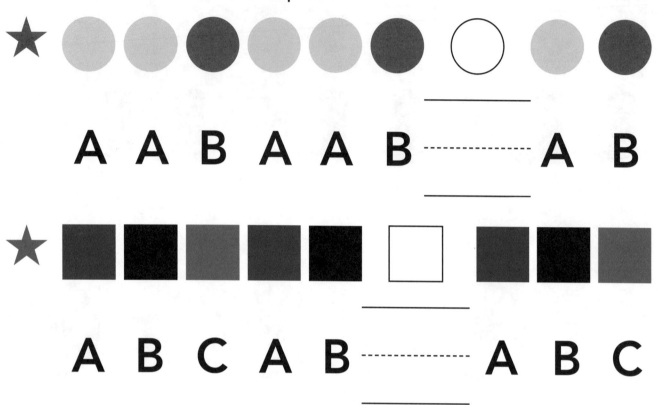

A A B A A B - - - - - - - A B

A B C A B - - - - - - - A B C

Circle the correct letter pattern.

ABB
ABC

AAB
ABC

Name ______________________________

Make Patterns 2.7

Make patterns.

★ AB

___	___	___	___	___	___
A	B	A	B	A	B

★ AAB

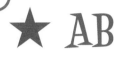

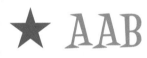

___	___	___	___	___	___
A	A	B	A	A	B

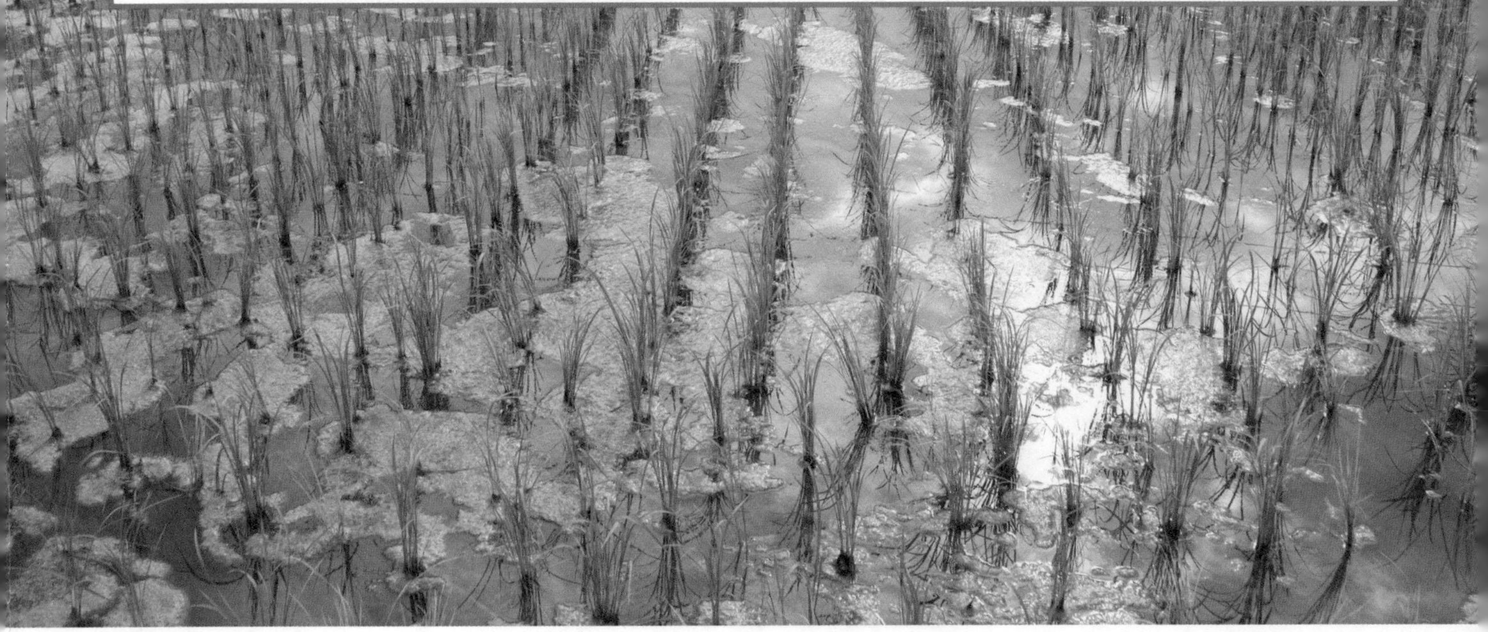

Make patterns.

Name _____

Listen and circle the patterns.

Circle the patterns.

Name _____

 Build.

⭐ Color to match.

★ Build.

★ Color to match.

Name _____

Listen and circle the AB and AAB patterns.

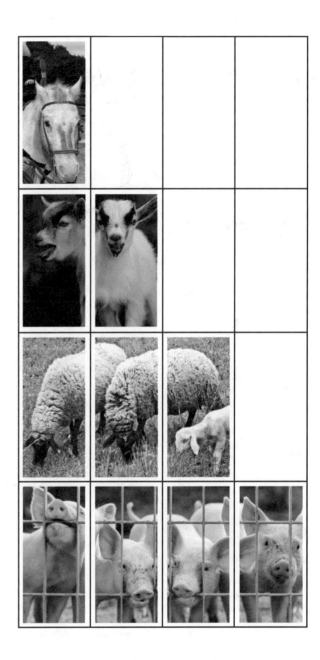

forty-seven **47**

Cut and glue the ABC pattern.

A B

A A B

A B B

A B C

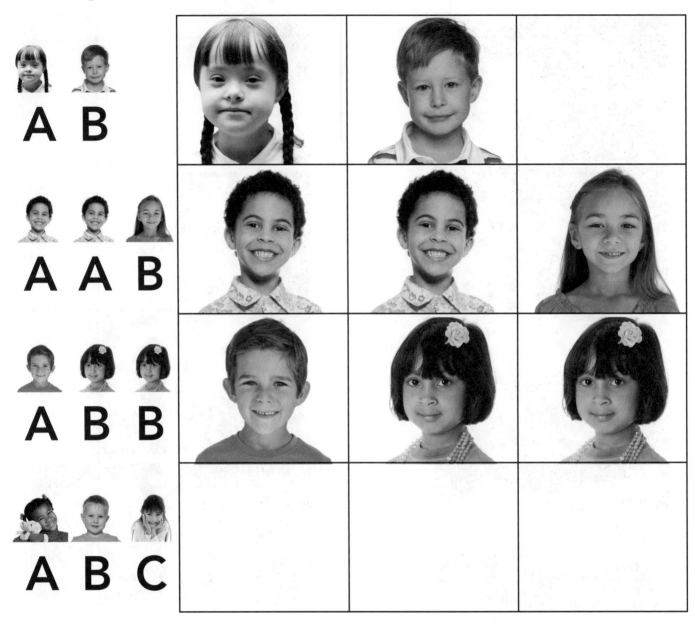

Color.

 Circle the patterns that are alike.

 Draw the pattern.

★ Copy the pattern.

_____

★ Color the pattern.

Draw and color shapes to match the patterns.

 color

     _____

 shape

   _____

 size

    _____

 color

    _____ _____

Draw lines to match the patterns to the letters.

AB

AAB

ABB

ABC

 Draw an AAB pattern.

Chapter 3
Count and Match

How precious to me are your thoughts, God!
Were I to count them, they would
outnumber the grains of sand.
Psalm 139:17a, 18a

Key Ideas:

Comparing Numbers: comparing number sets

Comparing Numbers: finding equal sets

Number Theory: counting forward from 1 to 10
and backward from 10 to 1

Color.

Match one to one.

Color one to one.

Draw to make the same number. Draw a line to match the objects one to one.

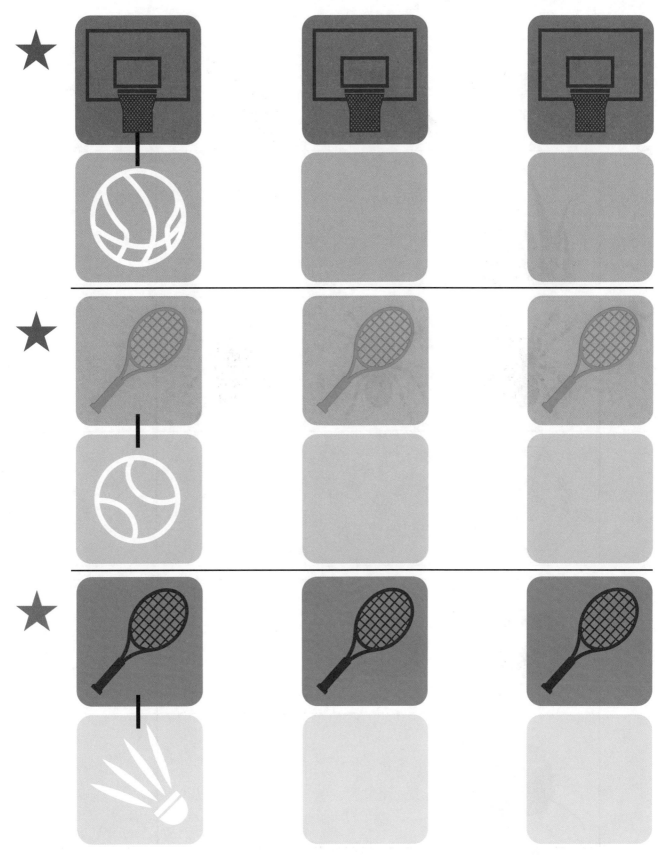

Draw to make the same number.

Name _____

More Than 3.3

Circle the group that has more than the other.

© *Mathematics* Kindergarten

fifty-nine **59**

Mark an X on the group that has more than the other.

Circle the group that has less than the other.

Draw a group that has less than the other.

⭐ teddy bears

⭐ butterflies

⭐ socks

Mark an X.

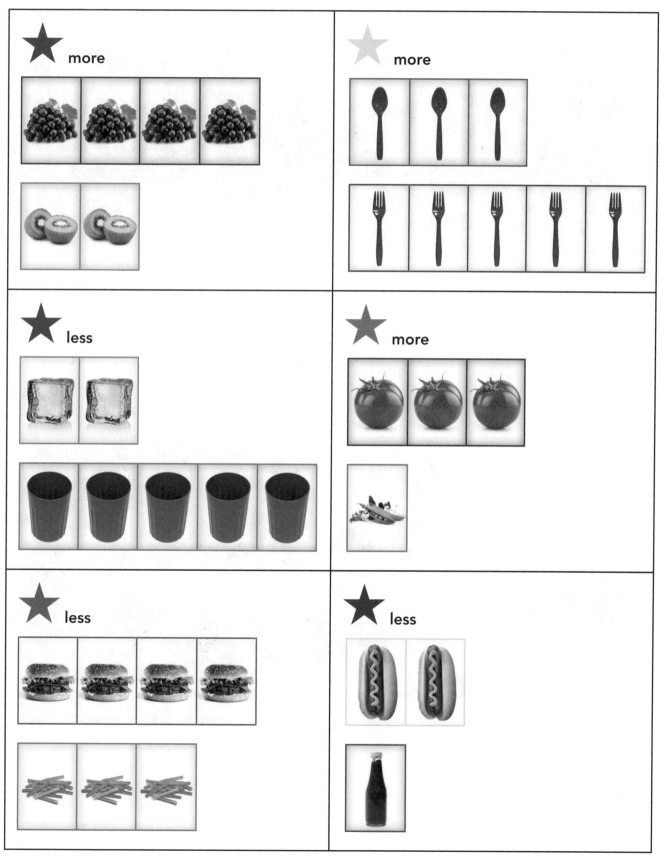

Draw and color.

⭐ **more than**

⭐ **less than**

Count and color.

Count and circle the group that has one more than the other.

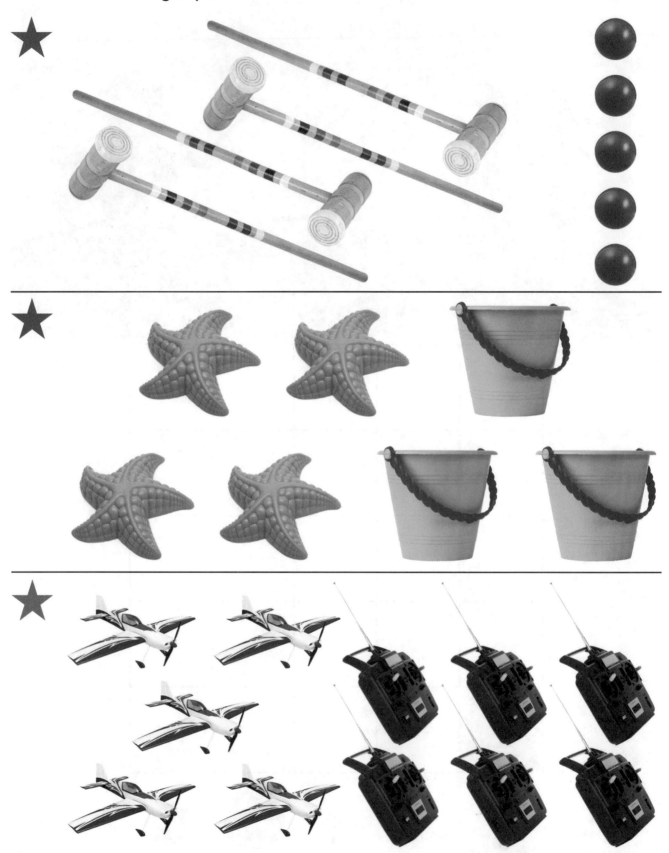

Count Forward and Backward  3.7

Count and color.

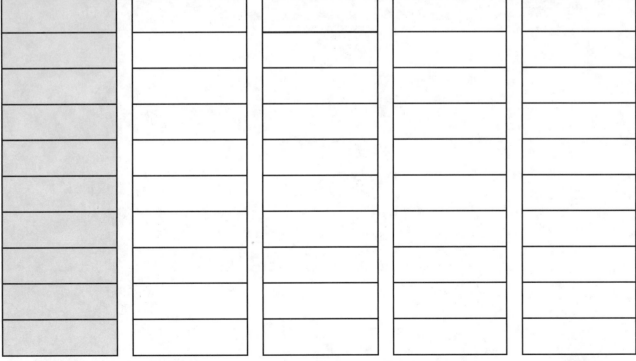

Mark the path from 1 to 10 using the ladybug dots.

Count and circle.

⭐ more than

⭐ less than

⭐ more than

Draw a line to the group that has one less than the other.

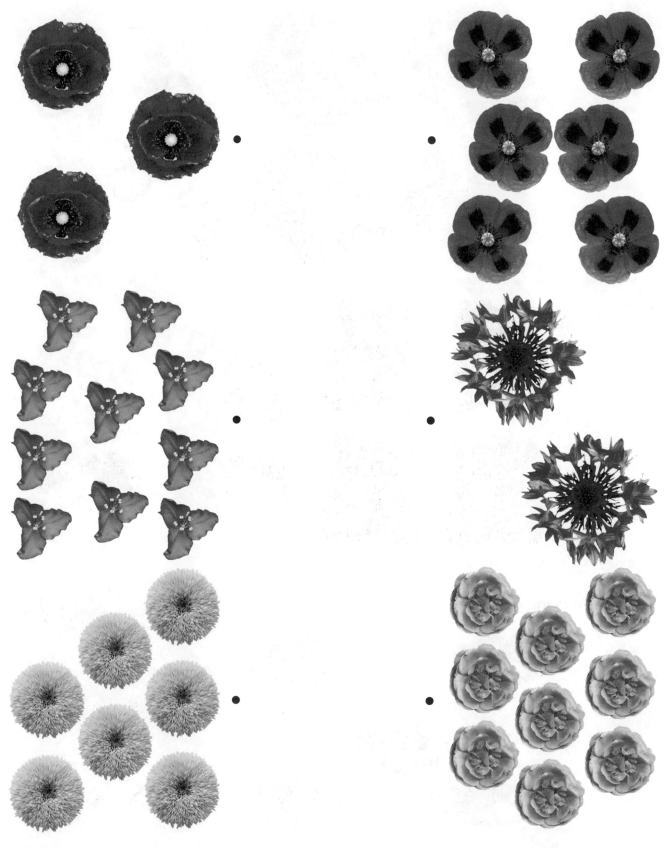

One More, One Less, and the Same 3.9

Circle and mark to make the same.

 one more

 one less

 one more

Draw and color.

⭐ **one more**

⭐ **same**

⭐ **one less**

Listen to the story and complete the graph.

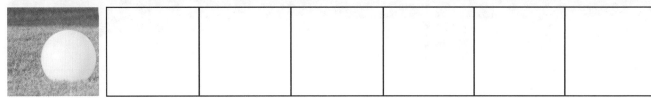

Count and graph the objects.

	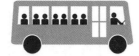		

Match one to one.

Count and circle.

 more

 less

 four

 seven

Draw.

 same

---

 one more

---

 one less

 Count and graph.

Name _____

Match one to one.

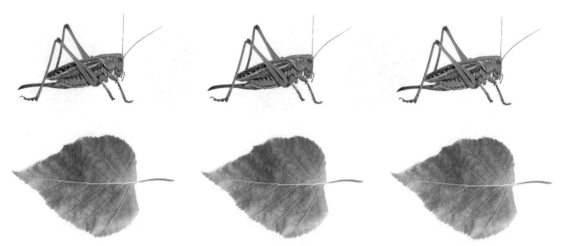

Circle.

 more

less

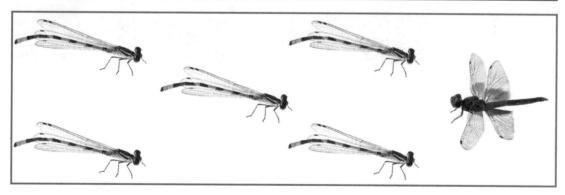

 three

 eight

Draw.

⭐ **same**

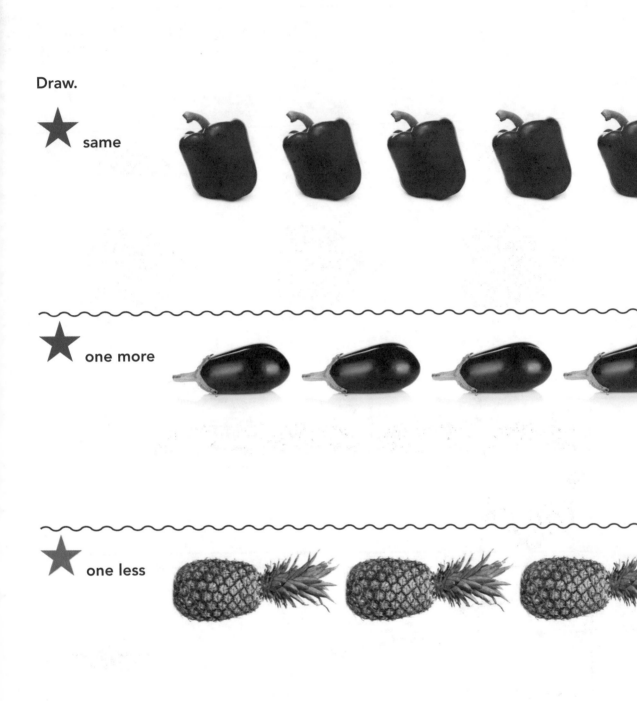

⭐ **one more**

⭐ **one less**

⭐ **Count and graph.**

Chapter 4
Numbers 0–5

Teach us to number our days, that we
may gain a heart of wisdom.
Psalm 90:12

Key Ideas:

Number Theory: identifying numbers 0–5

Number Theory: writing numbers 0–5

Number Theory: ordering numbers 0–5

Number Theory: distinguishing sets by number

Color.

MATH IN THE NEIGHBORHOOD

Name _____

Write. Draw a bone for the dog and a hose for each fire truck.

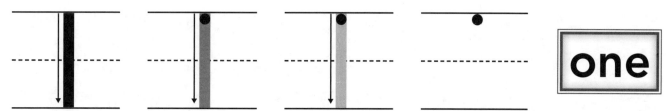

one

two

Circle the correct number.

Write and draw.

three

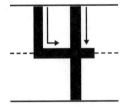 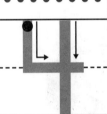 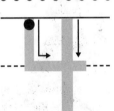 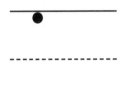

four

Count and draw lines to match.

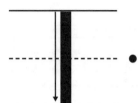

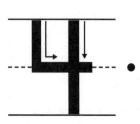

Name _____

Write and draw. Circle groups of 5.

5   5   5   _____   five

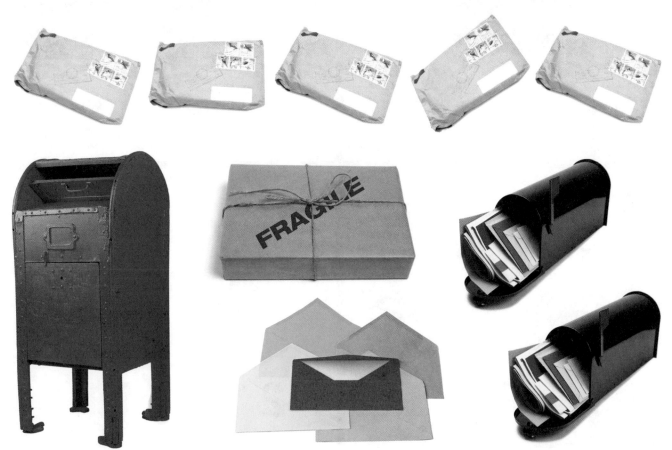

Circle the matching number.

1.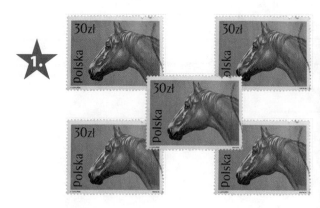

3   **5**   **2**

4.

4   **1**   **3**

2.

1   **2**   **3**

5.

5   **4**   **2**

3.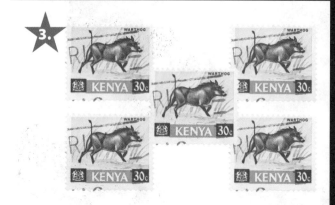

1   **3**   **5**

6.

2   **4**   **1**

Listen and write. Circle the objects that show 0.

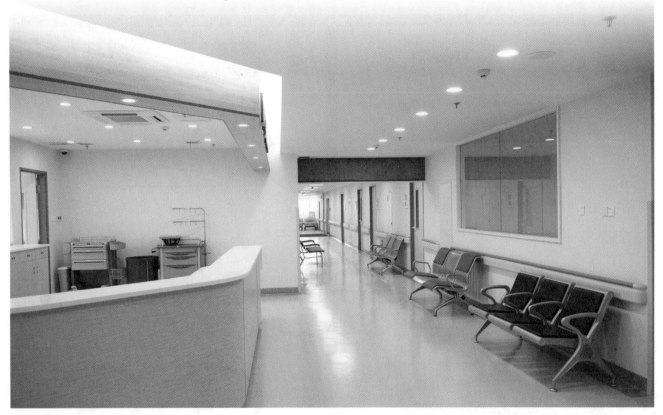

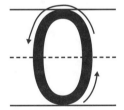  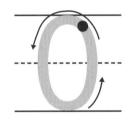 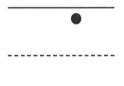 

zero

Count and write.

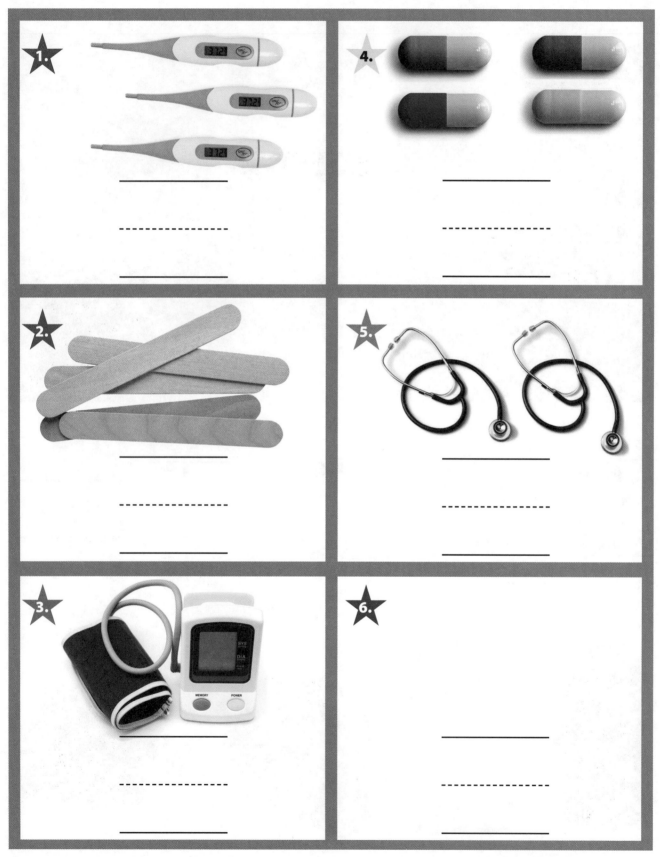

Name _____

Draw items or write the number.

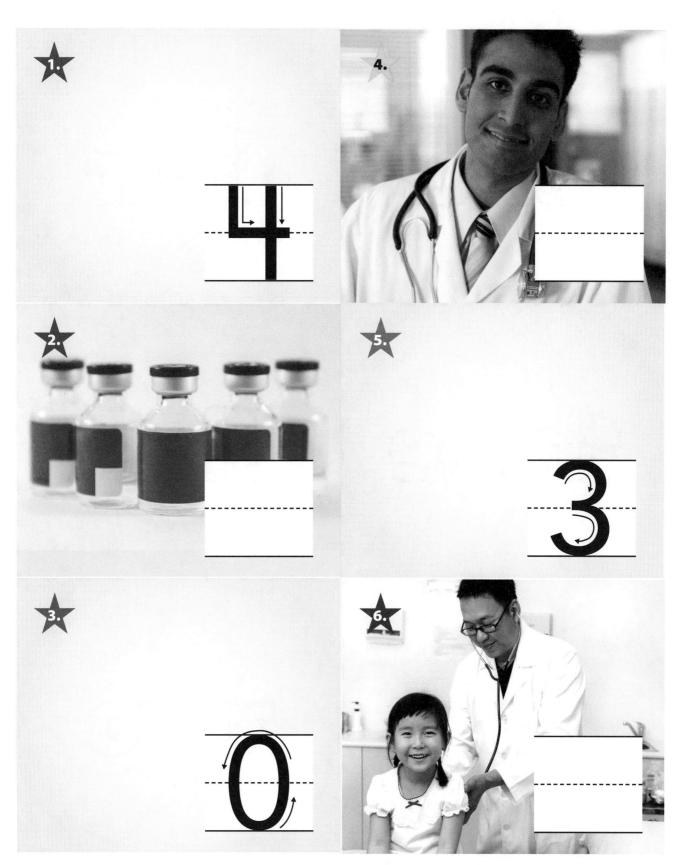

Color and cut.

one

four

three

five

two

zero

Order Numbers 0–5 4.6

Connect the dots in order.

Color a path from 0 to 5 to help Lin get to the library.

0	1	5	3
4	2	3	1
2	1	4	5

Write numbers in order from 0 to 5. Draw books.

Name _____

Compare Numbers 0–5 4.7

Count and write. Circle the objects.

 more

_____

- - - - - - - - - - - -

_____

- - - - - - - - - - - -

 less

_____

- - - - - - - - - - - -

_____

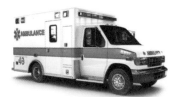  

- - - - - - - - - - - -

 more

_____

- - - - - - - - - - - -

_____

- - - - - - - - - - - -

_____

Draw one more. Count and write.

1. ⭐ _____
      - - - - - - - - - -
      _____

2. ⭐ _____
      - - - - - - - - - -
      _____

3. ⭐ _____
      - - - - - - - - - -
      _____

Circle the sets that match the number above.

3 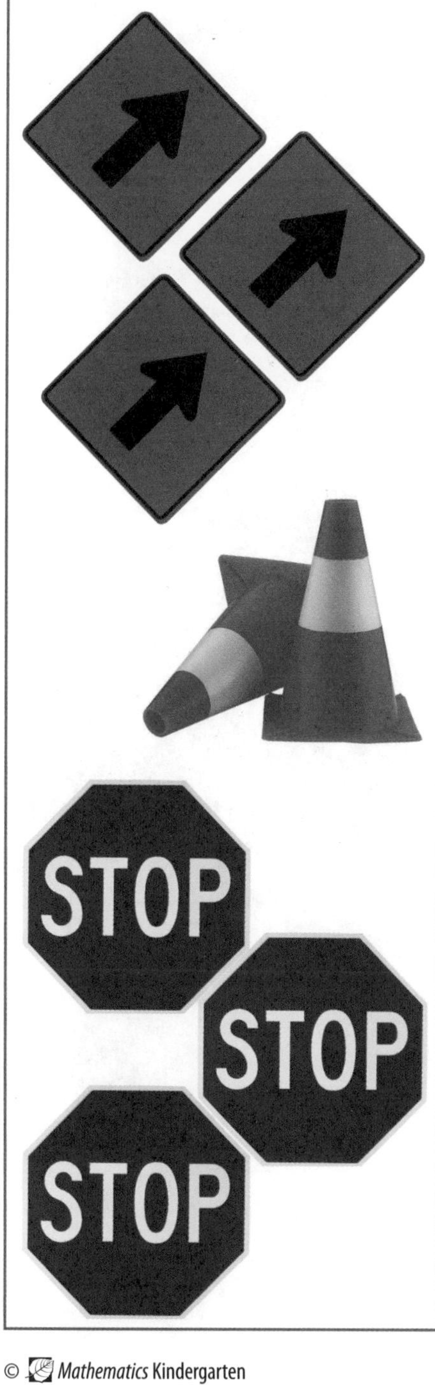	5 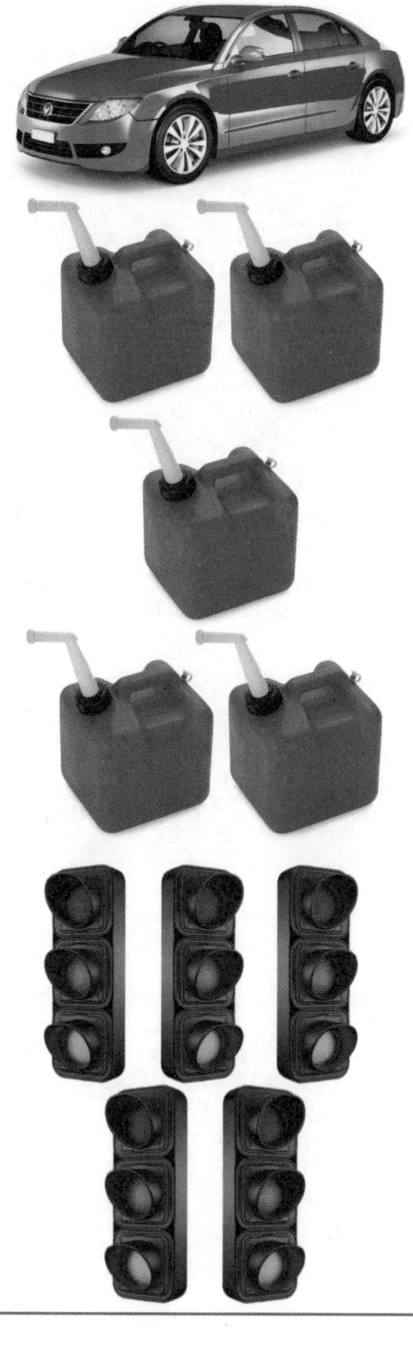	2 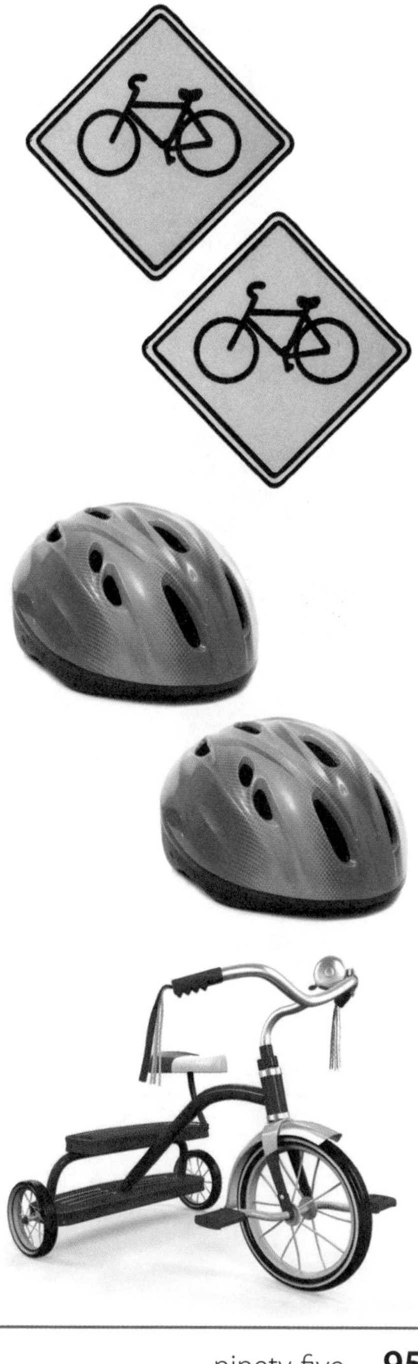

Circle the sets that match the number above.

4	0	1

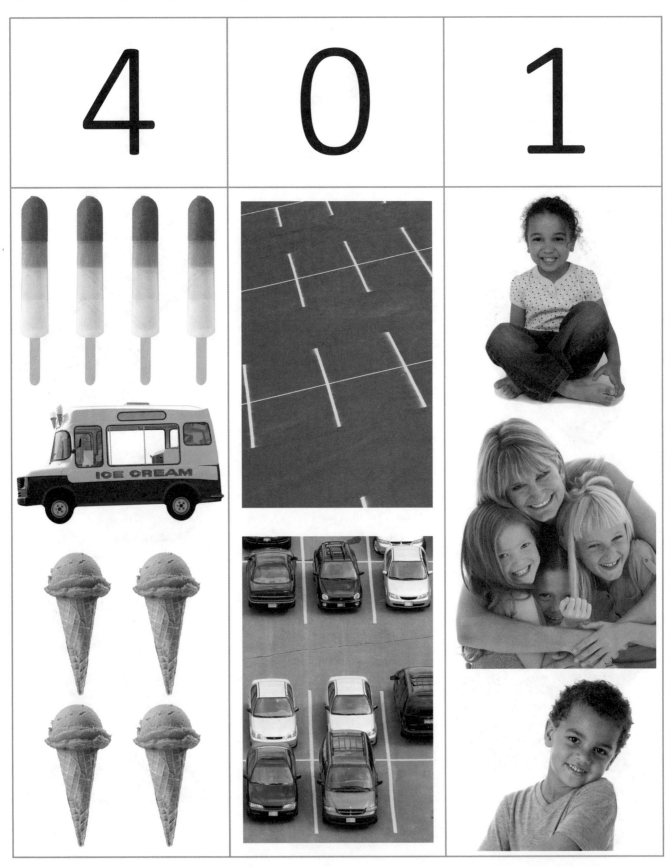

Write the missing numbers to help the sanitation worker finish his route.

Write the missing numbers.

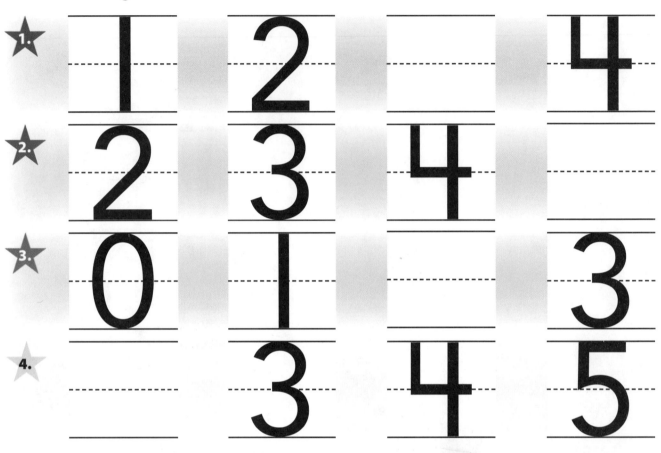

1. ⭐ 1   2   ___   4

2. ⭐ 2   3   4   ___

3. ⭐ 0   1   ___   3

4. ⭐ ___   3   4   5

Count the cars and trucks. Color the graph.

Count and write the numbers.

_____ _____ _____ _____ _____

- - - - - - - - - - - - - - - - - - - - - - - - - - - - - - - - - - - - - - - -

_____ _____ _____ _____ _____

Count and circle.

★ 1.

0 1 2

★ 2.

3 4 5

Count and write.

 ★ 3.

- - - - - - - - - - -

- - - - - - - - - - -

- - - - - - - - - - -

Draw.

 4.

5

Connect the dots.

⭐ **1.**

0
5
1
2
4
3

Circle more.

⭐ **2.**

Write the number and circle more.

⭐ **3.**

Write the number and circle less.

⭐ **4.**

Write the numbers.

⭐ **5.**

4 5
0 1

Count and circle.

0   1   2   3   4   5

Count and write.

- - - - - - - - - - -
═══════════

- - - - - - - - - - -
═══════════

- - - - - - - - - - -
═══════════

Draw.

- - - - 3 - - - -

Count and draw.

⭐ **1.**

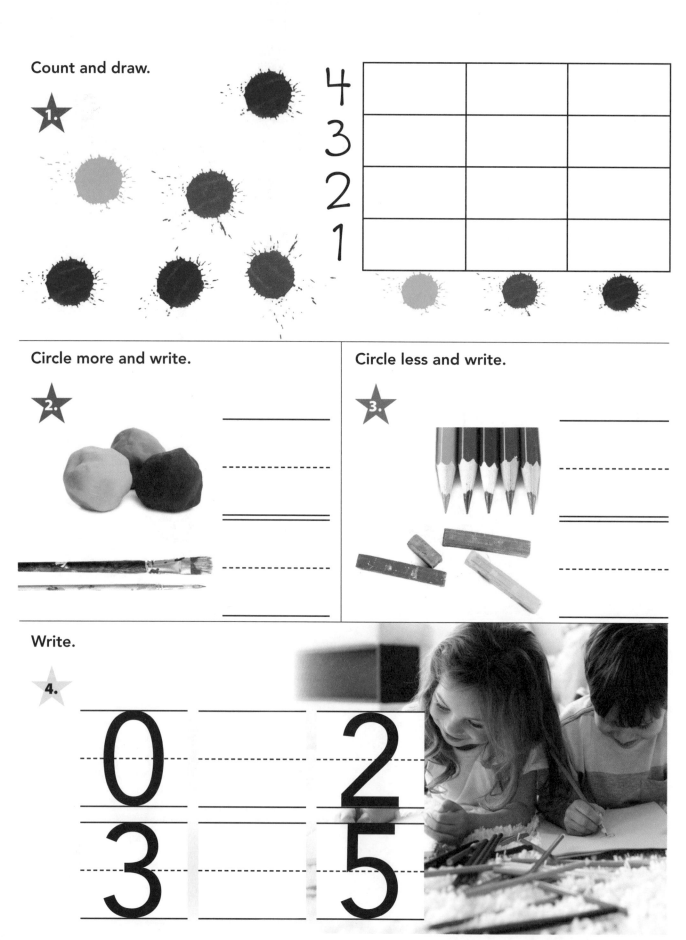

4
3
2
1

Circle more and write.

⭐ **2.**

_____

- - - - - - - -

═══════════

- - - - - - - -

_____

Circle less and write.

⭐ **3.**

_____

- - - - - - - -

- - - - - - - -

_____

Write.

⭐ **4.**

0

2

3

5

Chapter 5
Numbers 6–10

Does He not see my ways and
count my every step?
Job 31:4

Key Ideas:

Number Theory: identifying numbers 6–10

Number Theory: writing numbers 6–10

Number Theory: ordering numbers 6–10

Number Theory: distinguishing sets by number

Connect the dots.

MATH AT THE STORE

OPEN

1. Write and draw 6.

6 6 6 _____ | six |

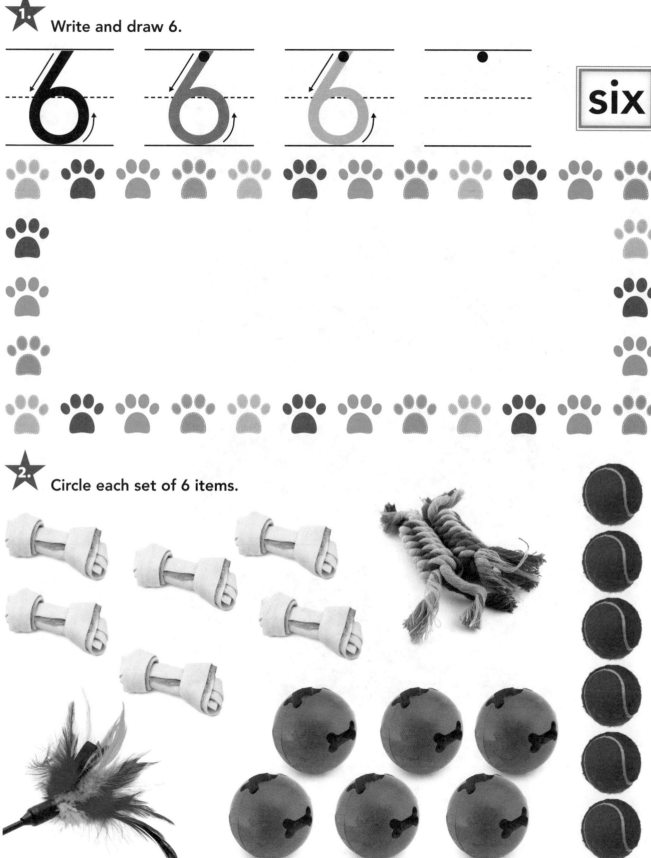

2. Circle each set of 6 items.

Count and circle how many there are.

1. 4
   5
   6

2. 4
   5
   6

3. 4
   5
   6

4. 4
   5
   6

5. Write the numbers 1 through 5.

_____ _____ _____ _____ _____

- - - - - - - - - - - - - - - -   - - - - - - - - - - - - - - - -   - - - - - - - - - - - - - - - -   - - - - - - - - - - - - - - - -   - - - - - - - - - - - - - - - -

_____ _____ _____ _____ _____

Name _____

 1. Write and draw 7.

seven

 2. Mark an X on each set of 7 fish.

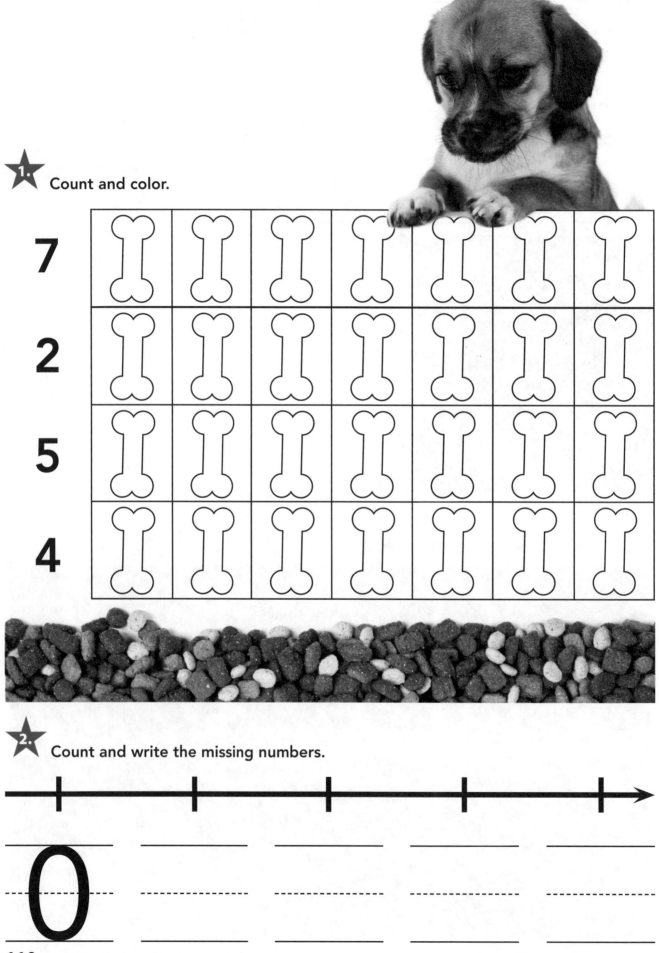

★ 1. Count and color.

7

2

5

4

★ 2. Count and write the missing numbers.

0 _ _ _ _ _

Write and draw 8.

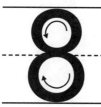 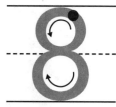 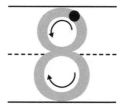 

eight

Use small objects to show each number.

six	seven	eight
five	four	three

Cut, count, and glue to match.

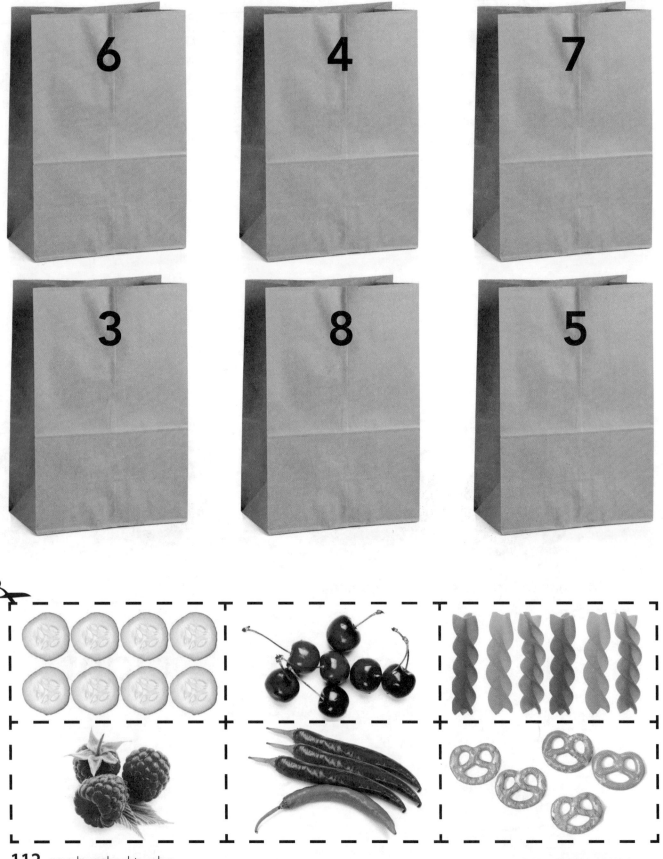

Name _____

 1. Write and draw 9.

    nine

 **2.** Trace 9 pieces of cereal.

Count and write the number of groceries on each shelf.

_____

- - - - - - - - - - - - -

_____

- - - - - - - - - - - - -

_____

- - - - - - - - - - - - -

_____

- - - - - - - - - - - - -

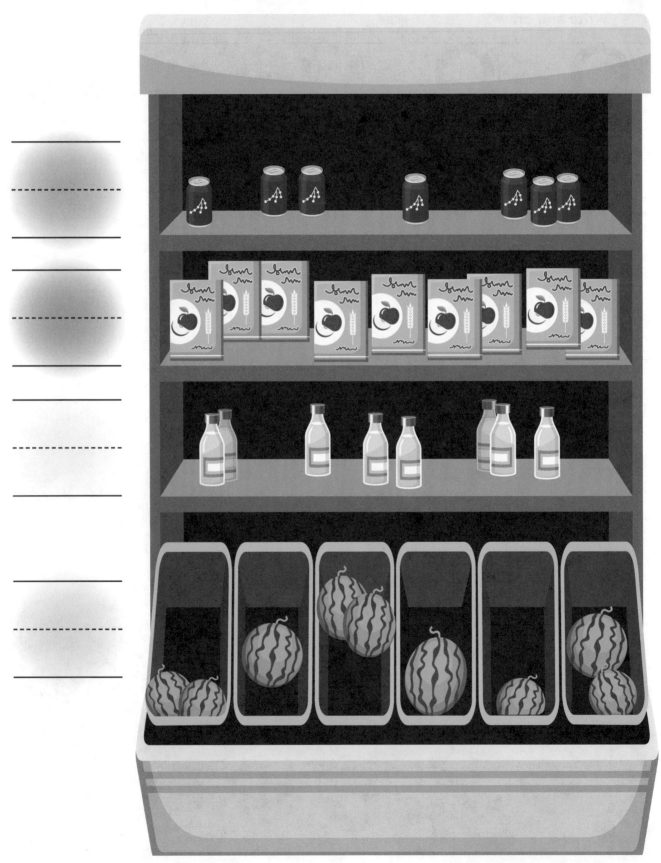

1. Write and draw 10.

 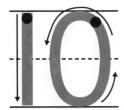 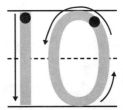 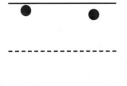

2. Circle the set of 10.

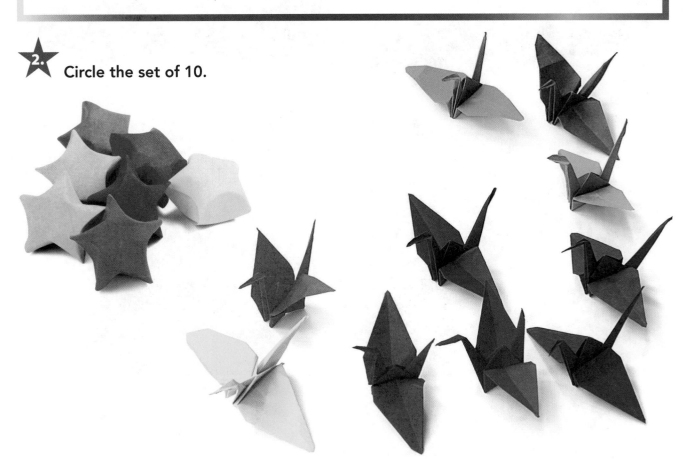

Count and circle the number that matches.

1.   3   4   5

2.   5   6   7

3.   8   9   10

4.   8   9   10

5.   2   3   4

6.   4   5   6

Name _____

Sequence Numbers 6–10 **5.6**

Write the number or draw.

9

_____

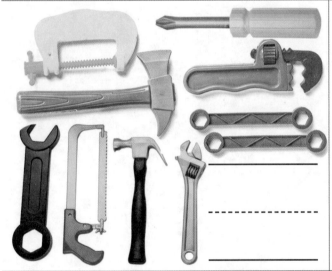

_____

8

_____

Color and cut.

✂ -

6
six

9
nine

8
eight

10
ten

7
seven

Color the rectangles to match the numbers.

0										
1										
2										
3										
4										
5										
6										
7										
8										
9										
10										

Help Manuel pay for his shoes. Trace the numbers in order.

| 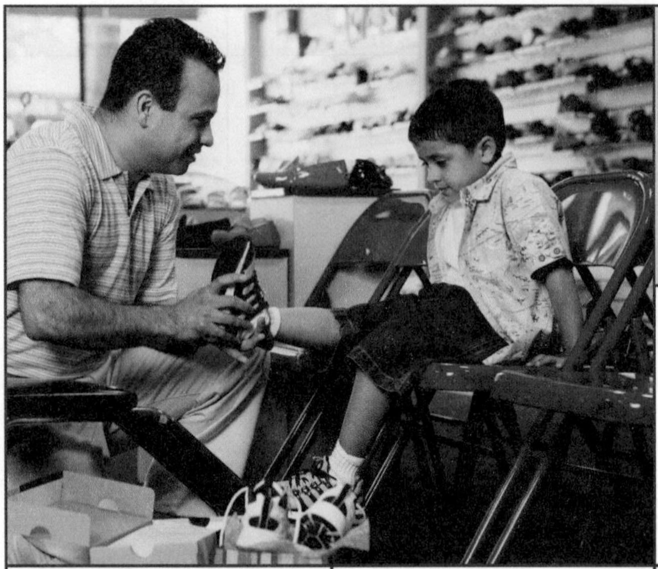 0 | 0 |
| 1 | 2 |

| 3 | 2 | 4 | 3 |
| 10 | 6 | 5 | 0 |

| 8 | 7  |
| 9 | 10 |

Name _____

Circle the number that is more than the other.

 1.

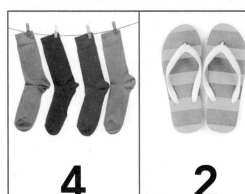

4   2

 3.

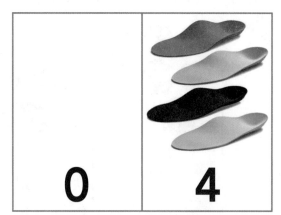

0   4

 2.

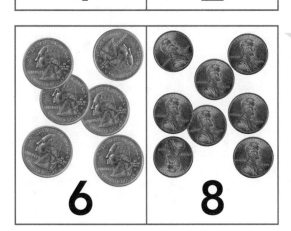

6   8

 4.

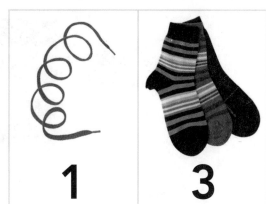

1   3

Draw more. Write the number.

 5.

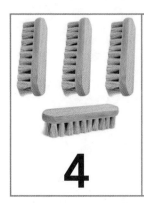

4

_____

- - - - - - - - - - - - - - -

_____

 6.

7

_____

- - - - - - - - - - - - - - -

_____

Mark an X on the number that is less than the other.

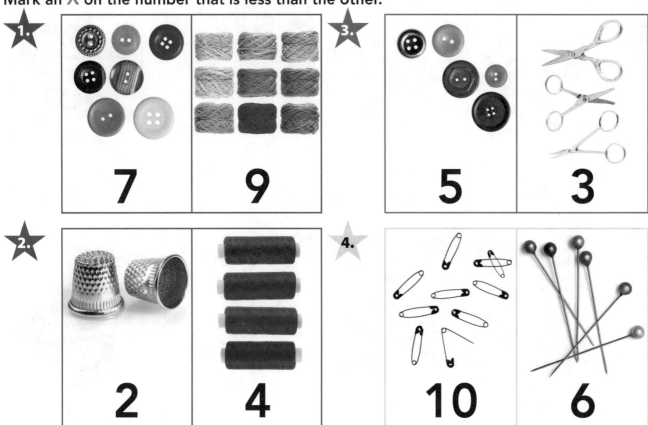

⭐ 1.

7   9

⭐ 3.

5   3

⭐ 2.

2   4

⭐ 4.

10   6

Draw less. Write the number.

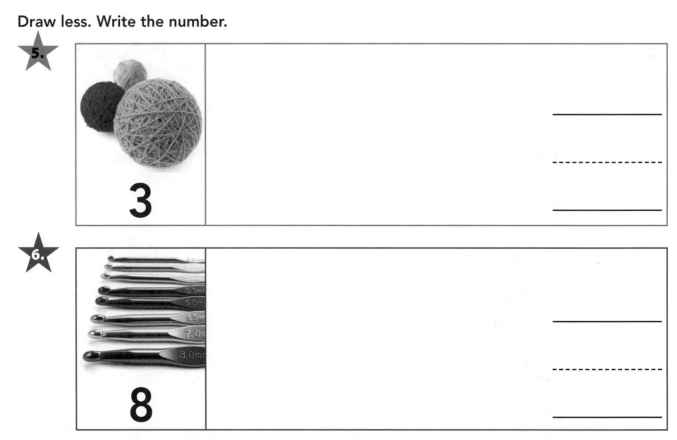

⭐ 5.

3

⭐ 6.

8

Cut.

one	six	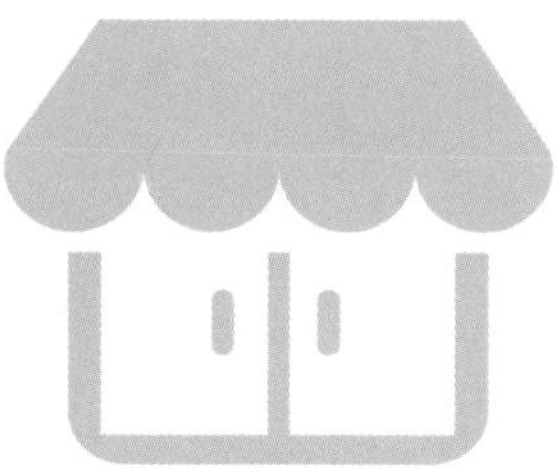	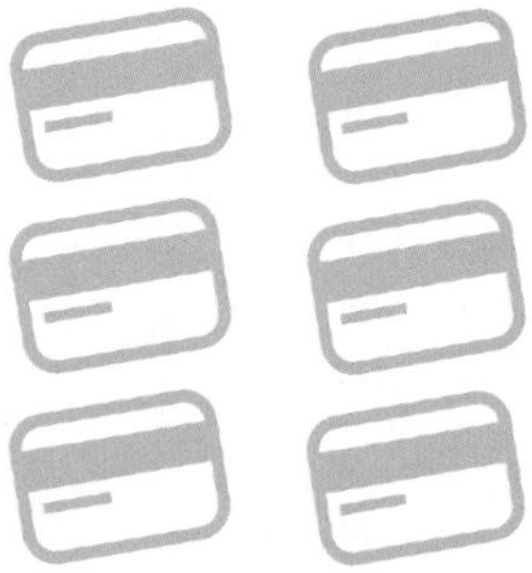
two	seven	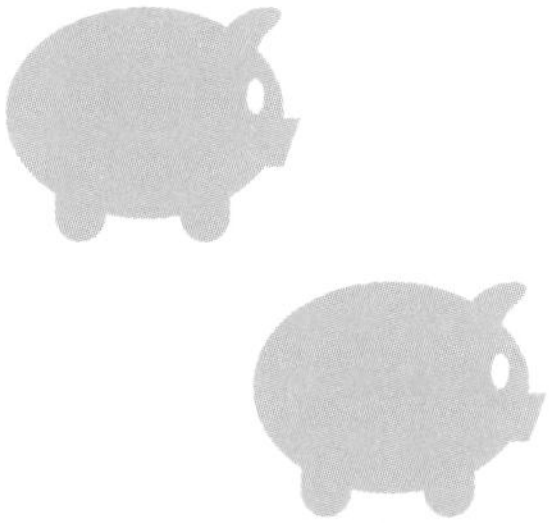	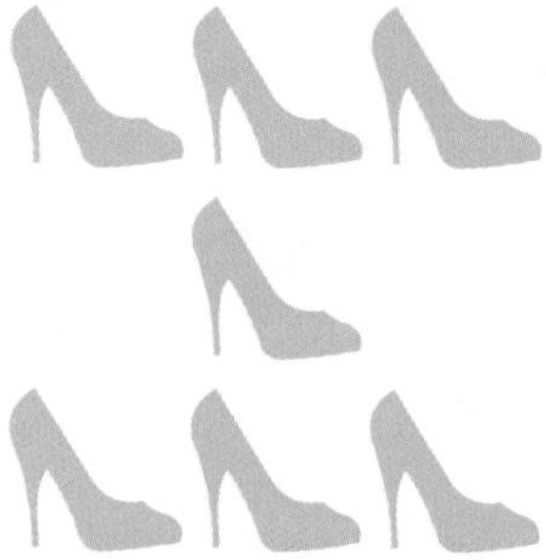
three	eight	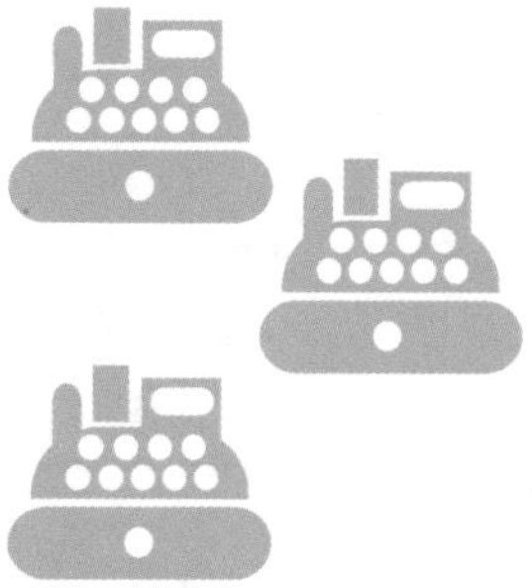	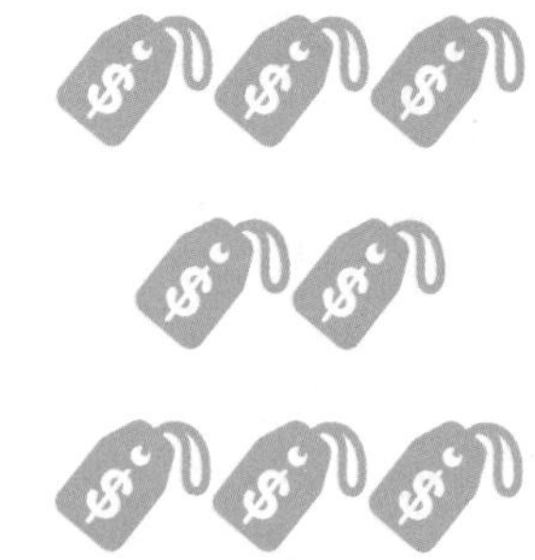
four	nine	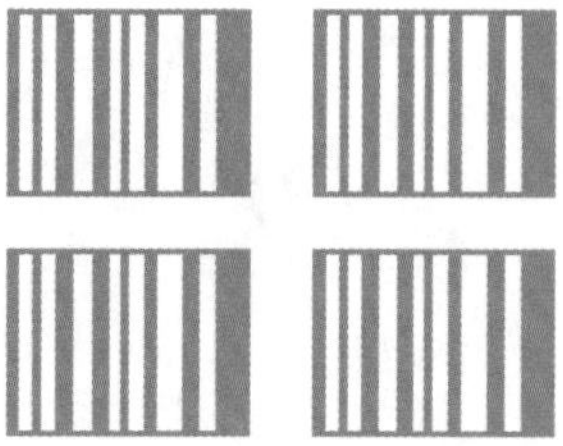	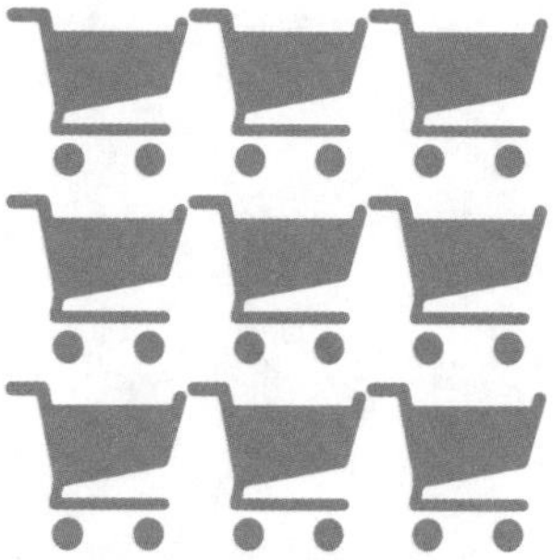
five	ten	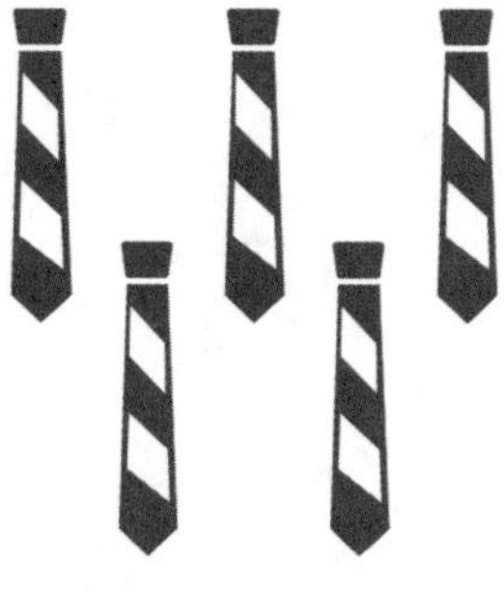	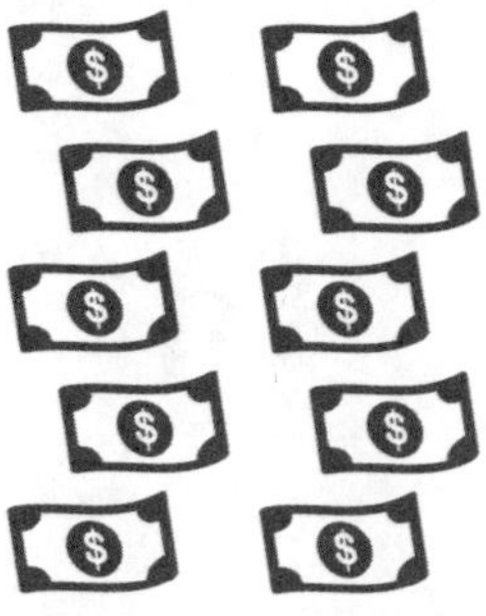

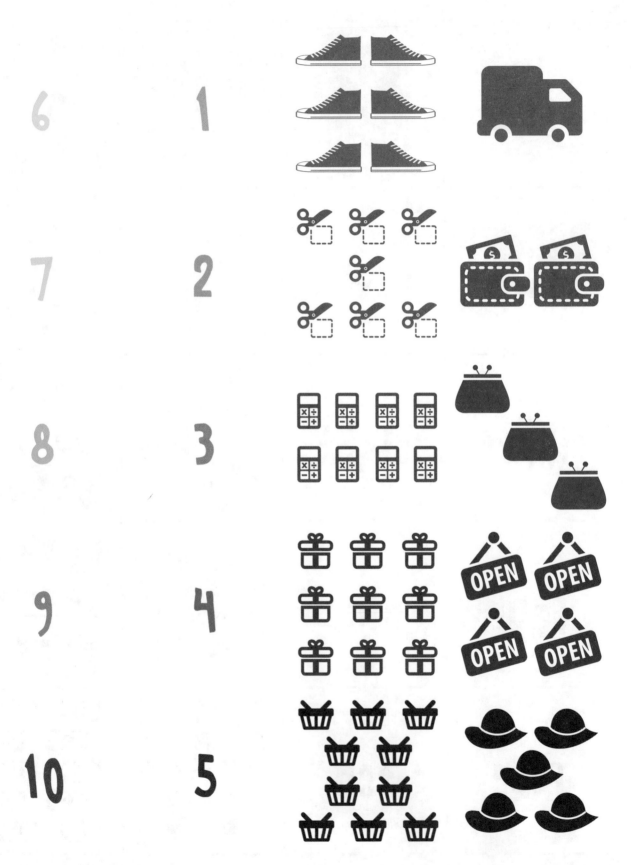

6   1

7   2

8   3

9   4

10   5

Numbers Before, After, and Between 5.10

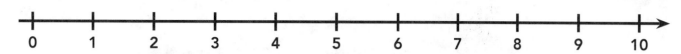

Write the number before.

 1. _ _ _ _ _ _ _ _ _ **7**

 2. _ _ _ _ _ _ _ _ _ **4**

Write the number after.

 3. **6** _ _ _ _ _ _ _ _ _

4. **2** _ _ _ _ _ _ _ _ _

Write the number between.

 5. **8** _ _ _ _ _ _ _ _ **10**

 6. **2** _ _ _ _ _ _ _ _ **4**

Circle the missing numbers.

★ 1.	2	__	4	3	6	7
★ 2.	7	8	__	10	6	9
★ 3.	0	__	2	4	0	1
★ 4.	8	9	__	9	10	0
★ 5.	__	1	2	4	3	0

Count and write.

_____   _____   _____   _____

- - - - - - - -   - - - - - - - -   - - - - - - - -   - - - - - - - -

_____   _____   _____   _____

Count and circle more.

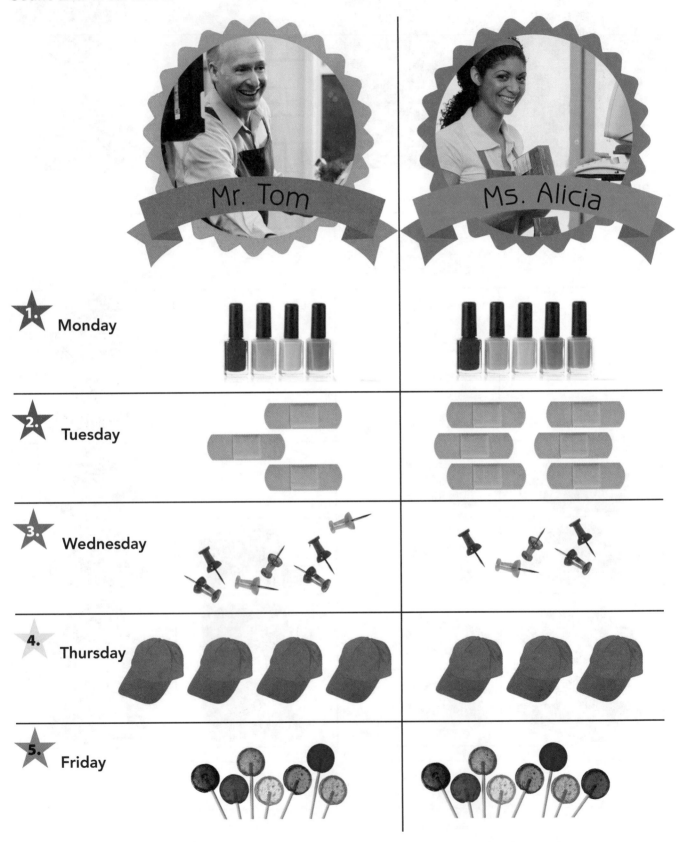

Mr. Tom

Ms. Alicia

1. **Monday**

2. **Tuesday**

3. **Wednesday**

4. **Thursday**

5. **Friday**

⭐ **1.** Circle the correct number of items in each set.

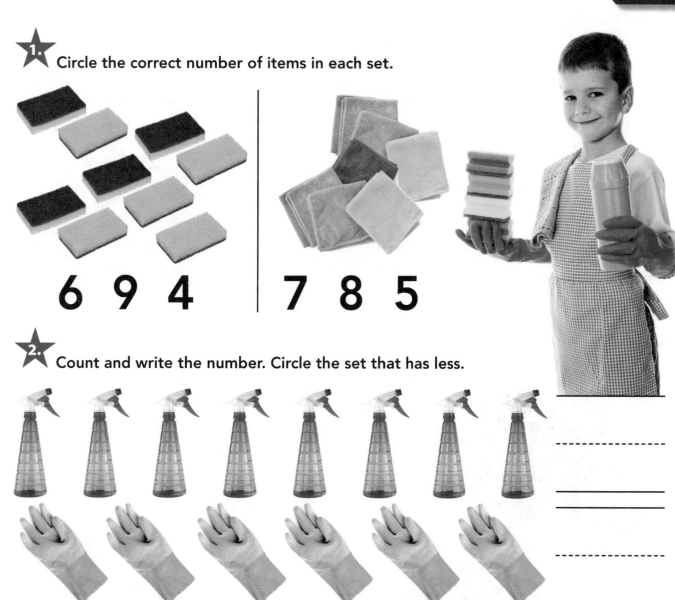

6 9 4 | 7 8 5

⭐ **2.** Count and write the number. Circle the set that has less.

⭐ **3.** Count and write the number. Circle the set that has more.

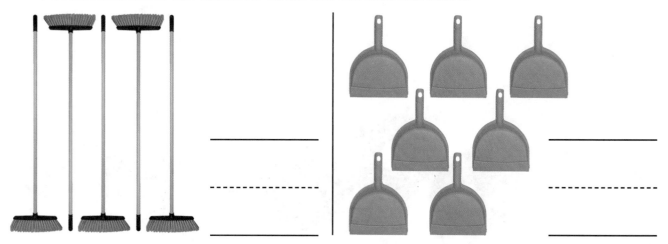

⭐ **1.** Listen and use the color your teacher says to circle the number.

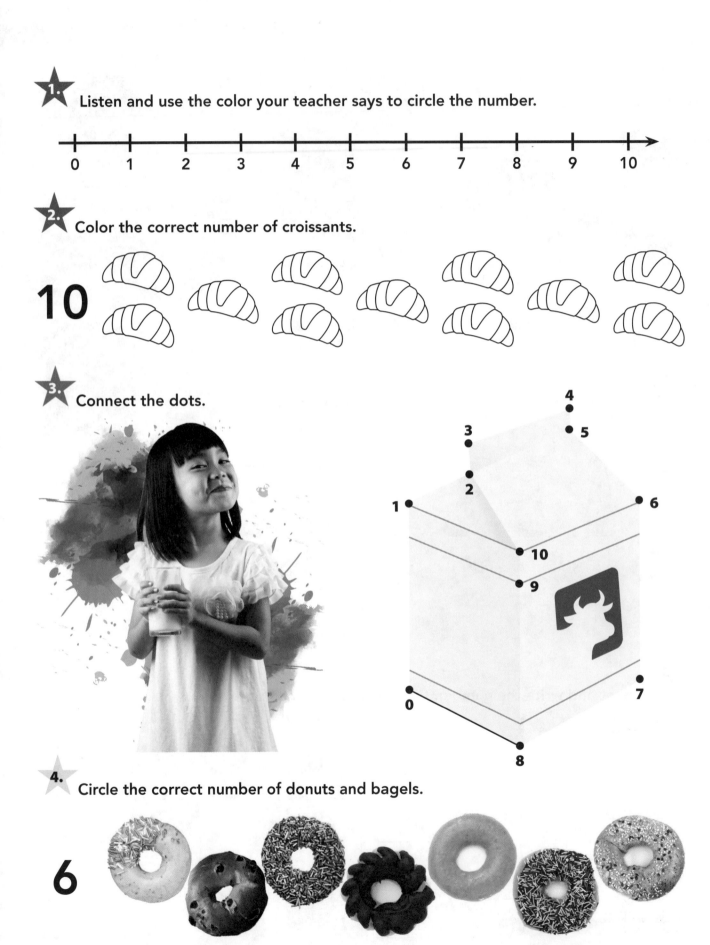

0   1   2   3   4   5   6   7   8   9   10

⭐ **2.** Color the correct number of croissants.

10

⭐ **3.** Connect the dots.

4
3   5
2   6
1   10
9
0   7
8

⭐ **4.** Circle the correct number of donuts and bagels.

6

⭐ **1.** Circle the correct number of items in each set.

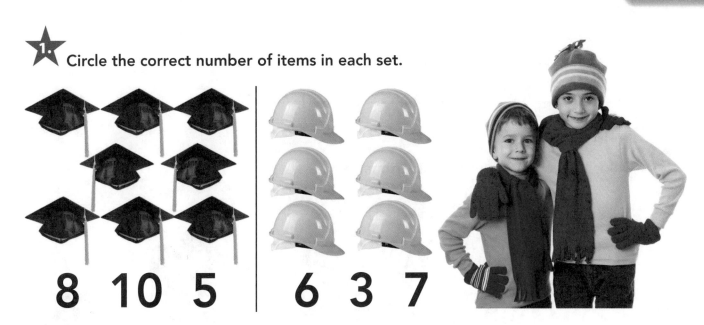

8 10 5   6 3 7

⭐ **2.** Count and write the number. Circle the set that has less.

_____

- - - - - - - - - - - - -

_____

- - - - - - - - - - - - -

_____

⭐ **3.** Count and write the number. Circle the set that has more.

_____

- - - - - - - - - - - - -

_____

- - - - - - - - - - - - -

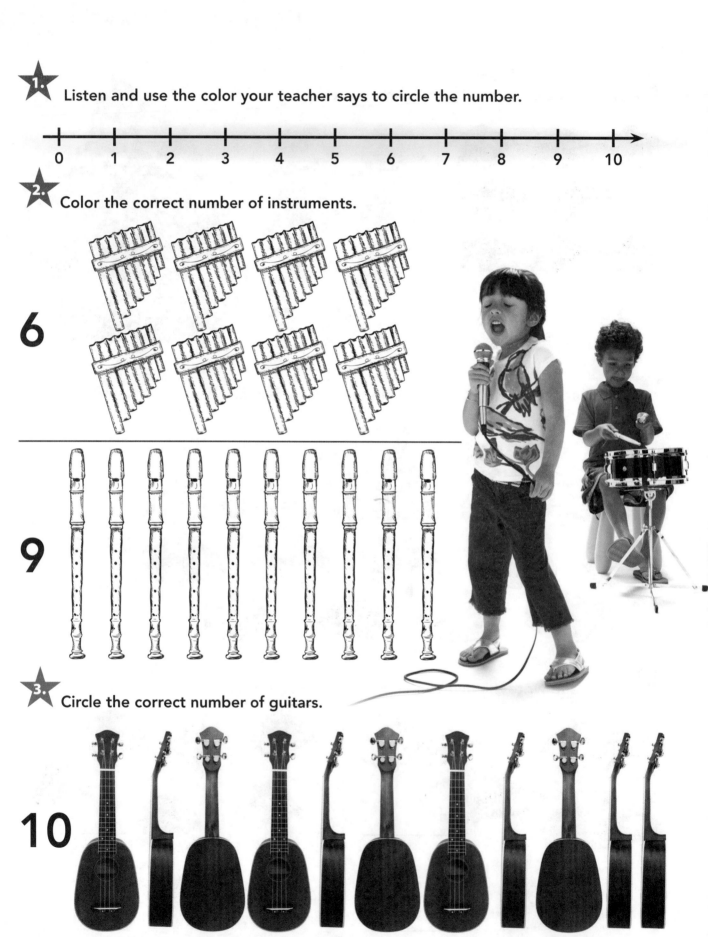

1. Listen and use the color your teacher says to circle the number.

0 1 2 3 4 5 6 7 8 9 10

2. Color the correct number of instruments.

6

9

3. Circle the correct number of guitars.

10

Chapter 6
Solids, Shapes, and Equal Parts

I praise You because I am fearfully and wonderfully made; Your works are wonderful, I know that full well.
Psalm 139:14

Key Ideas:

Geometry: classifying geometric shapes by attribute

Geometry: identifying patterns of slides, flips, and turns

Geometry: identifying symmetry

Find the shapes. Circle.

MATH AT A BIRTHDAY PARTY

Key

circle

cone

cylinder

triangle

sphere

Name _____

Solids 6.1

Circle the object that matches the shape.

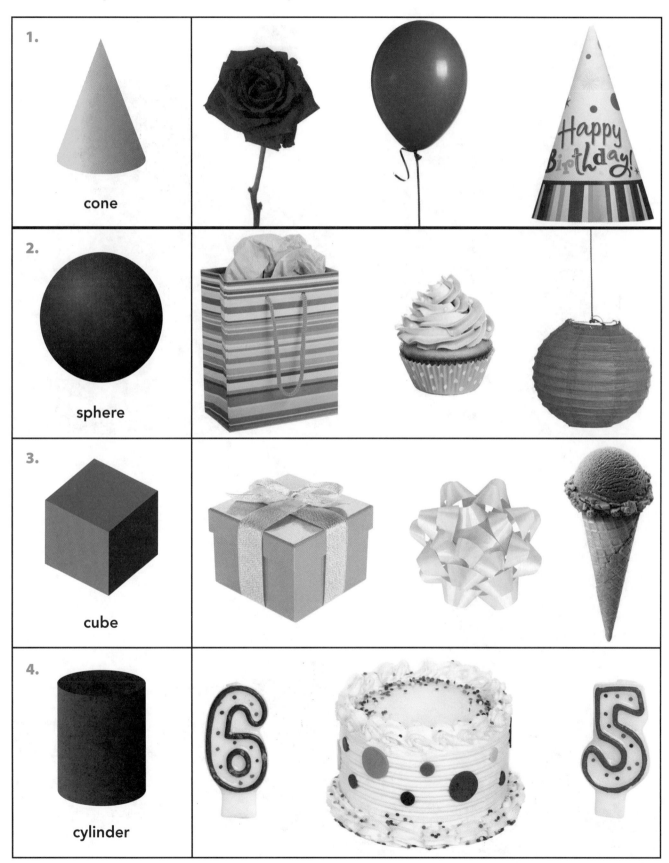

1. cone

2. sphere

3. cube

4. cylinder

© Mathematics Kindergarten

one hundred thirty-five **135**

Find the shapes in the pictures. Mark an X.

1. sphere

2. cone

3. cylinder

4. cube

Name _____

Draw lines to match the shapes.

1.

2.

3.

4.

Color the shapes.

Name _____

Trace the shape that each face makes.

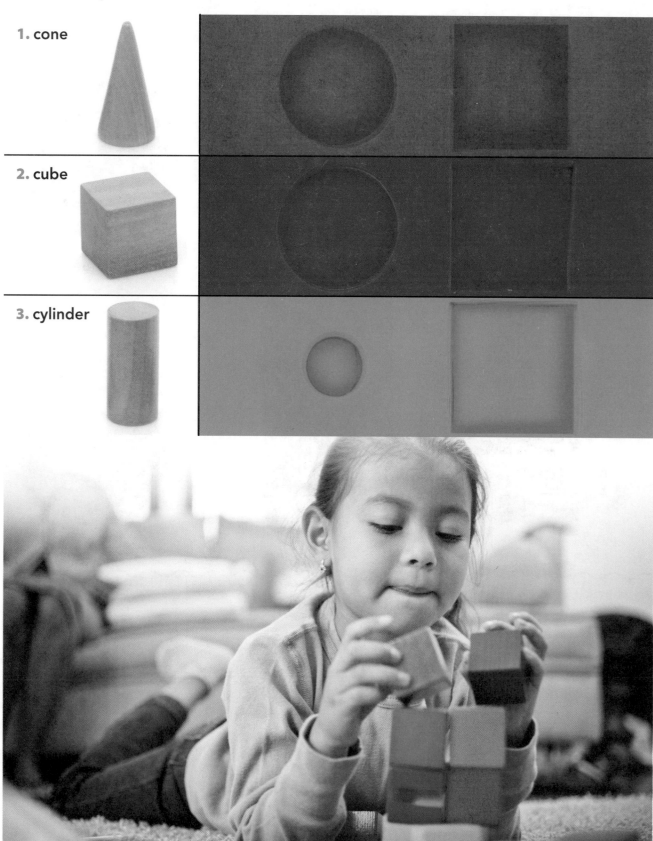

1. cone

2. cube

3. cylinder

Circle each solid that makes the shape.

1.

cone   cube

2.

cylinder   cube

3.

cube   cylinder

Make Shapes in Solids 6.4

Draw the shape of the shadows.

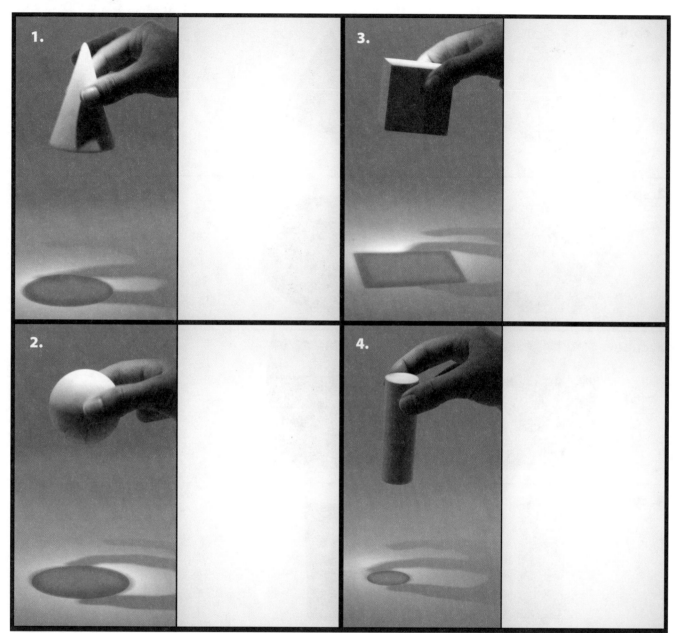

1.

2.

3.

4.

Cut and glue to match the shapes.

1. cone

2. sphere

3. cube

4. cylinder

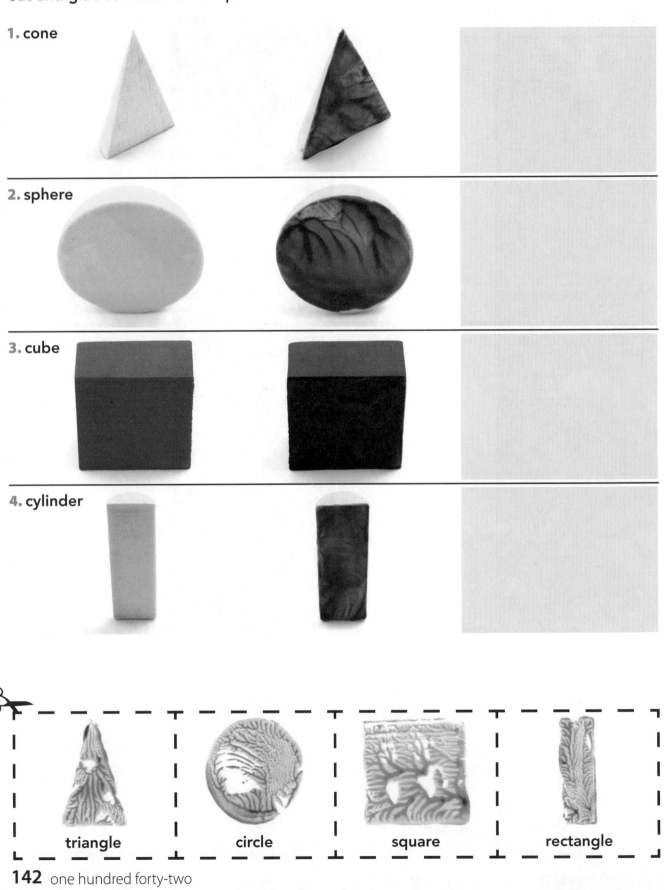

✂

triangle   circle   square   rectangle

Name _____

Plane Shapes 6.5

Circle the matching shapes.

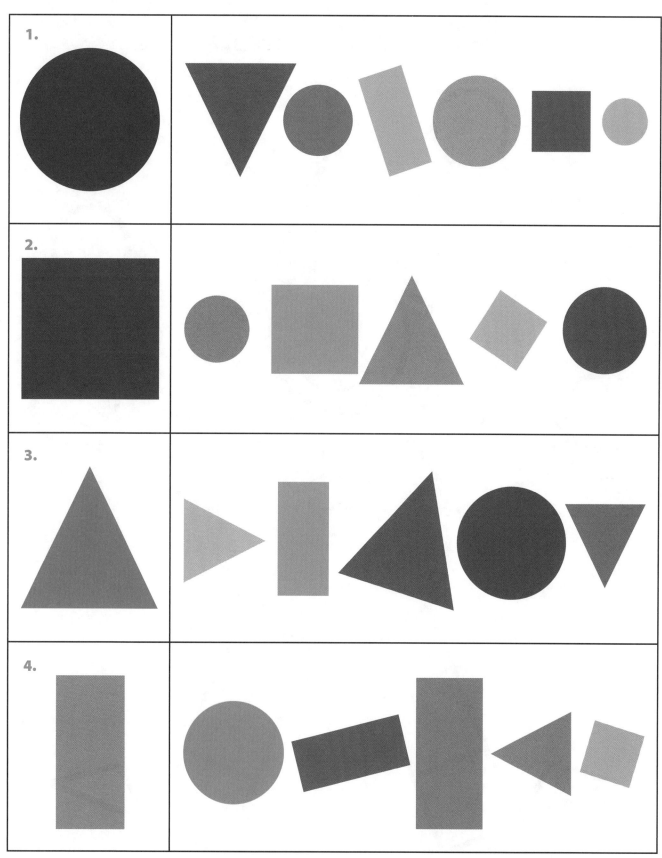

1.

2.

3.

4.

Color the shapes.

Name _____

Squares and Rectangles 6.6

Circle the number.

1. squares

3   4   5

2. rectangles

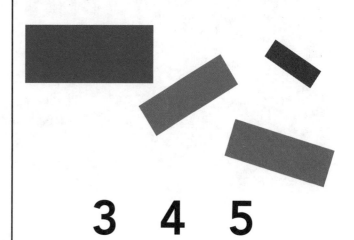

3   4   5

Write the number of shapes in the flags.

3. Chile

_____   _____

- - - - - - - - - - ☐   - - - - - - - - - - ☐

_____   _____

4. United Arab Emirates

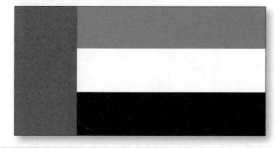

_____   _____

- - - - - - - - - - ☐   - - - - - - - - - - ☐

_____   _____

5. Uruguay

_____   _____

- - - - - - - - - - ☐   - - - - - - - - - - ☐

_____   _____

© Mathematics Kindergarten

one hundred forty-five **145**

Write the number of shapes in the flag.

1. Central African Republic

Color the shapes inside the Christian flag.

2.   Key

| blue | |
| red | |

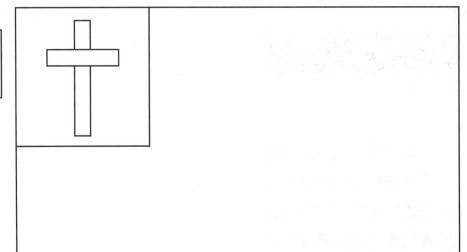

Circles and Triangles 6.7

Circle the number.

1. circles

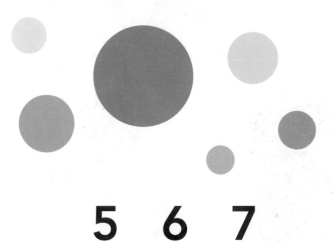

5   6   7

2. triangles

5   6   7

Write the number of shapes in the flags.

3. Laos

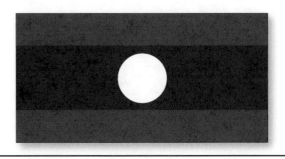

_____ ◯   _____ △

4. Jamaica

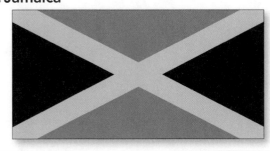

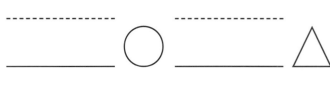

_____ ◯   _____ △

5. Niger

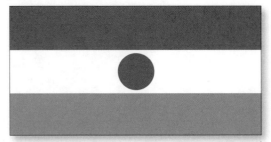

_____ ◯   _____ △

Write the number of shapes in the flag.

1. Philippines

_____   _____

- - - - - - - - - - - - - - ○   - - - - - - - - - - - - △
_____   _____

Draw a flag. Write the numbers of shapes you used.

2.

_____   _____   _____   _____

- - - - - - - - - □   - - - - - - - - - △   - - - - - - - - - ○   - - - - - - - - - ▯
_____   _____   _____   _____

Mark an X on each picture that does not show equal parts.

1.
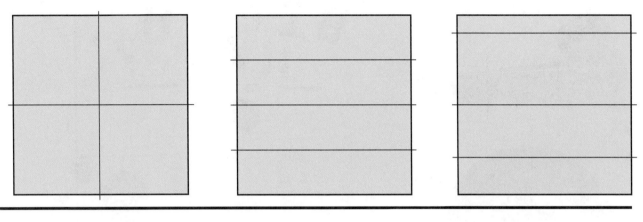

2.
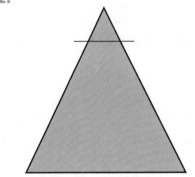 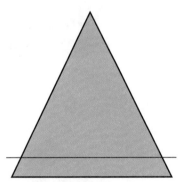 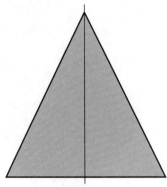

3.
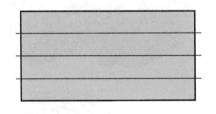 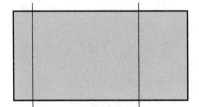 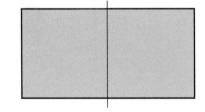

4.
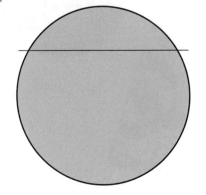 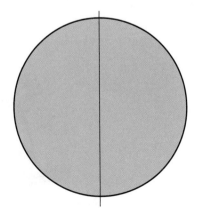 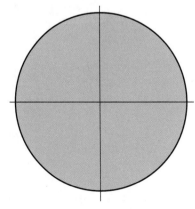

Circle each picture that shows equal parts.

Draw equal groups on each plate.

Draw a line to match the items to a party bag so the bags are equal.

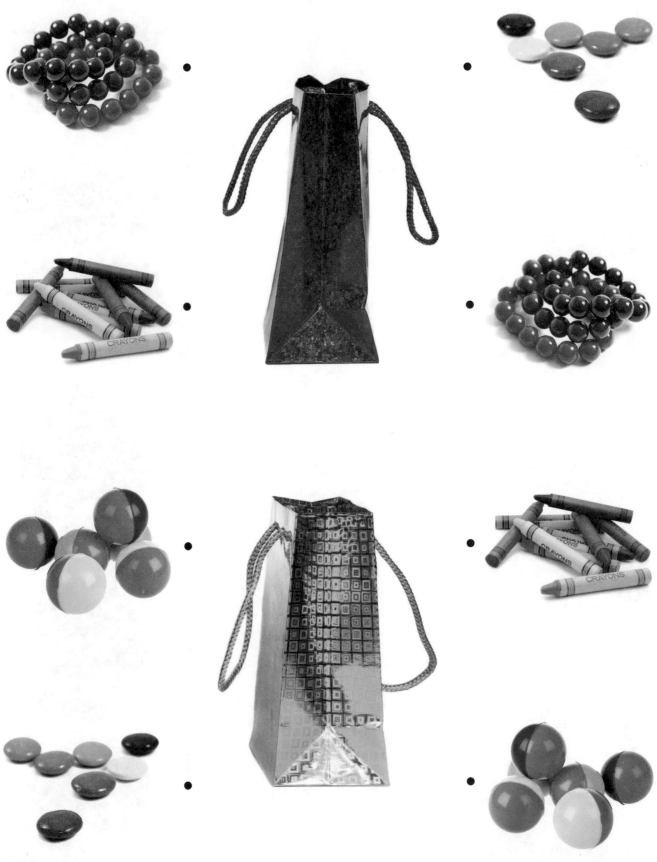

Circle the picture that shows one half of the first shape.

Draw the other half.

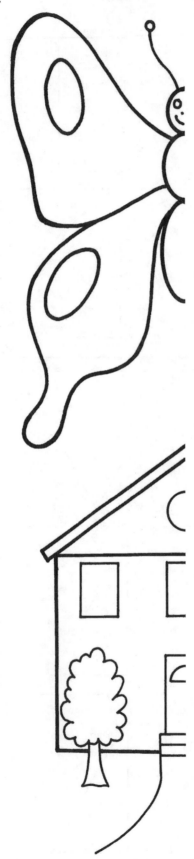

Slides, Flips, and Turns `6.11`

Slide the parrot.

Flip the parrot.

1.

★

2.

★

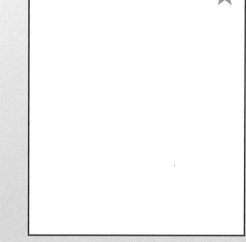

✂

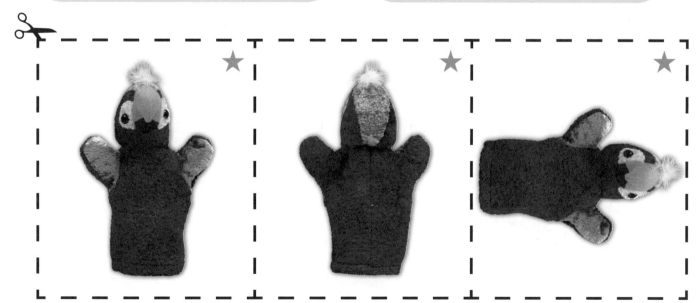

★   ★   ★

1. Turn the parrot.

2. Look at each uncolored half. Color the slide blue. Color the flip green. Color the turn red.

Name _____

Pattern Block Shapes 6.12

Use pattern blocks to fill in each picture. Circle the shapes used. Color.

1.

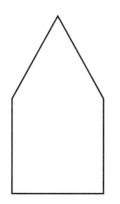

2.

3.

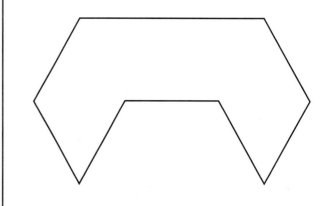

4.

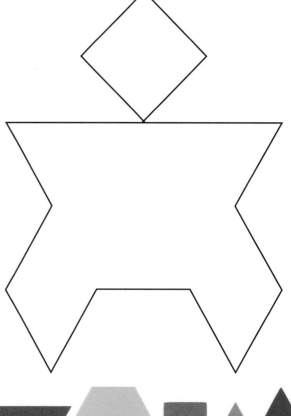

1. Use pattern blocks to fill in the dog.

2. Use pattern blocks to make a picture.

Name _____

Circle the objects that match the shape.

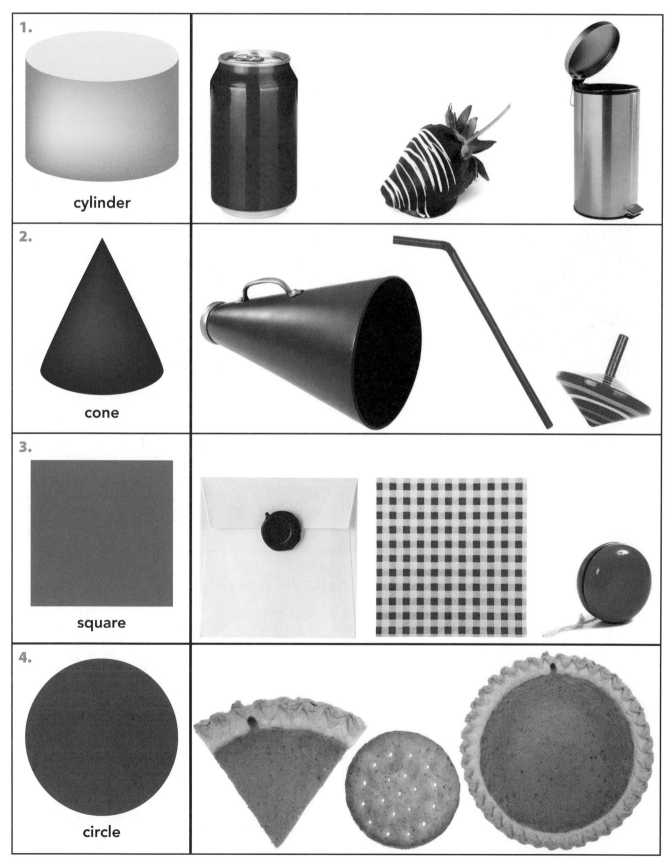

1. cylinder

2. cone

3. square

4. circle

1. Draw the other half.

2. Color the shapes to match the pattern blocks.

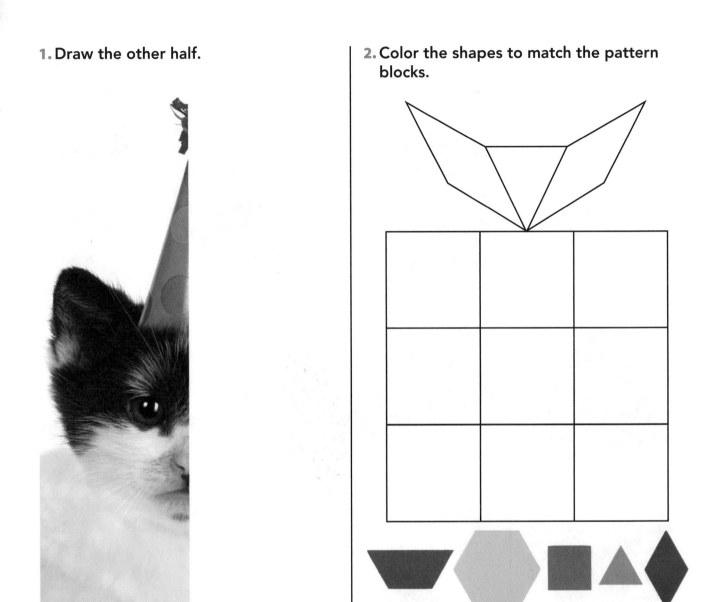

3. Color the turn blue. Color the flip green. Color the slide red.

Match the objects to their shapes.

1.

sphere
•

2.

cube
•

3.

cylinder
•

•

•

•

•

•

4.

rectangle
•

5.

triangle
•

6.

circle
•

•

•

•

Circle half.

1.

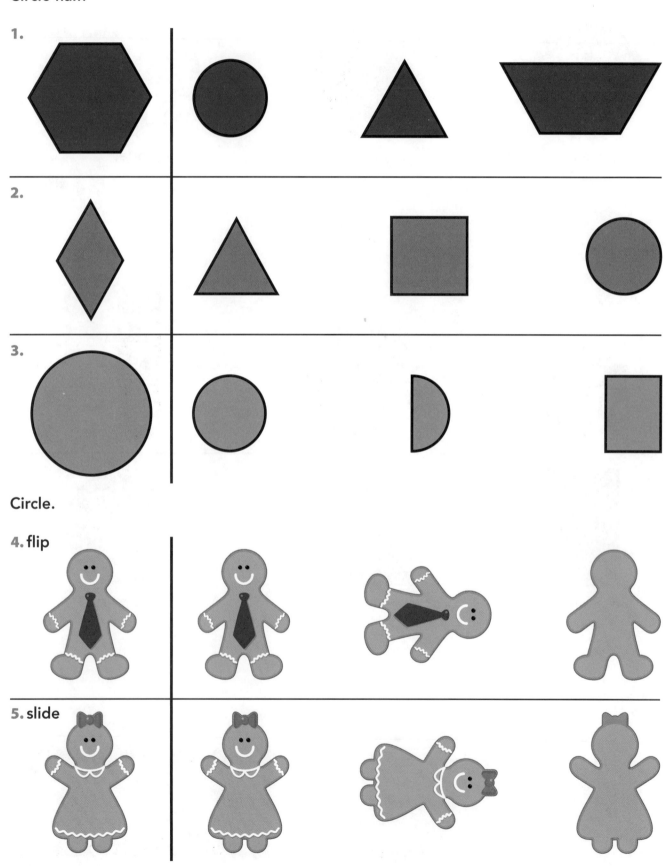

2.

3.

Circle.

4. flip

5. slide

Chapter 7
Look at Larger Numbers

He determines the number of the stars
and calls them each by name.
Psalm 147:4

Key Ideas:

Number Theory: read and write numbers to 31

Number Theory: count numbers to 100

Place Value: read and write numbers to the tens place

Place Value: model two-digit numbers

Place Value: use a number chart to find numbers greater than or less than

Guess the number of people. Then count the people.

MATH AT SPORTING EVENTS

Guess.   Count.

_____   _____

----------------   ----------------

_____   _____

Count 10 and some more. Trace the numbers.

1.

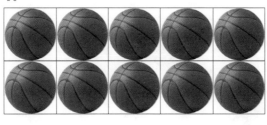 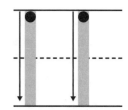

2.

3.

  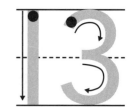

4.

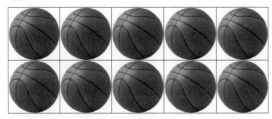  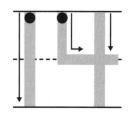

5.

  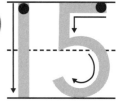

Count and write the number of balls.

1.

_____
- - - - - - - - - - -
_____

2.

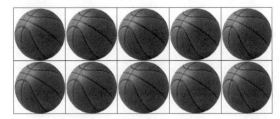 

_____
- - - - - - - - - - -
_____

Draw balls to show each number.

3.

15

4.

13

Identify and Write 16–19 7.2

Count 10 and some more. Trace the numbers.

1.
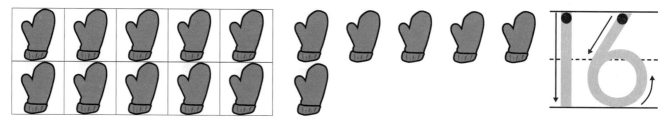

2.

3.
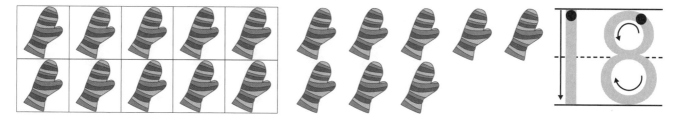

4.

Count. Circle the number.

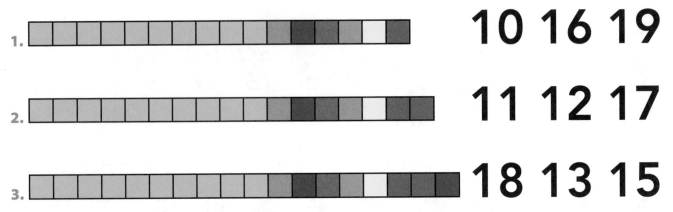

1. 10 16 19

2. 11 12 17

3. 18 13 15

Circle 10. Count and write the number.

4.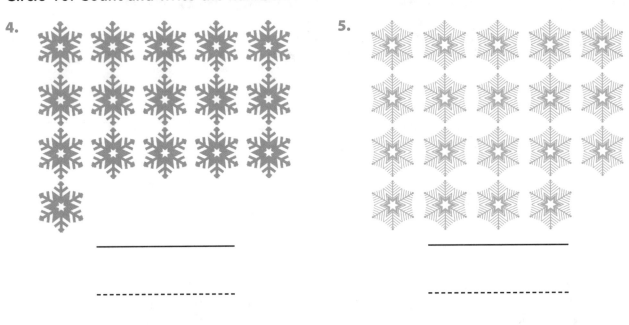

_____

- - - - - - - - - - - - - - - - - - - -

_____

5.

_____

- - - - - - - - - - - - - - - - - - - -

Color the tens blue. Color the ones purple.

6.

How many?

_____

- - - - - - - - - - - - - - - - - - - -

_____

Name _____

Count. Trace and write the number.

1.

Draw more to show 20.

2.

3.

Count and color 20.

4.

Listen and use the number line to count and mark the numbers.

1.

11 12 13 14 15 16 17 18 19 20

Count and write the number.

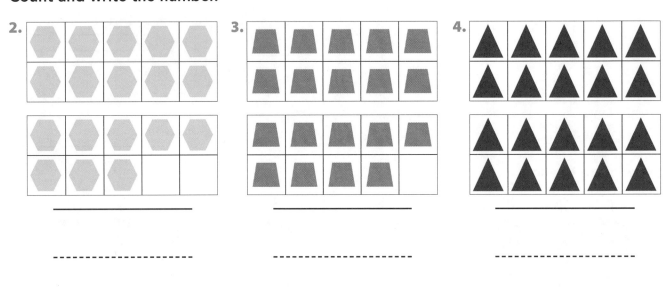

2.

3.

4.

_____   _____   _____

- - - - - - - - - - - - - - - - - -   - - - - - - - - - - - - - - - - - -   - - - - - - - - - - - - - - - - - -

_____   _____   _____

Connect the dots. Start at 1.

5.

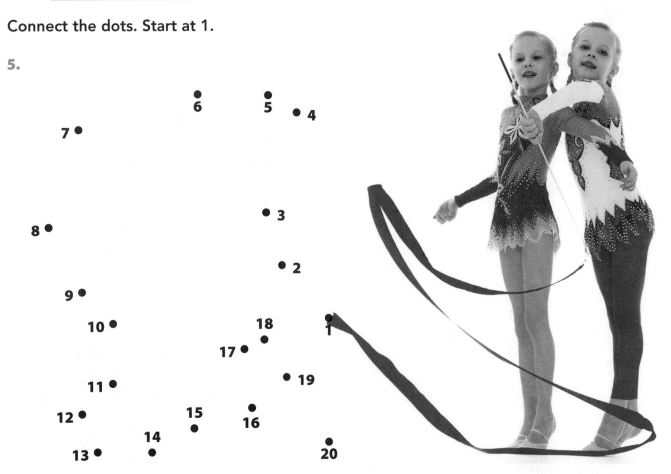

6 5 4

7

8

3

2

9

10 18

17 1

11 19

12 15 16

14

13 20

Name _____

Count. Trace the numbers.

1.    21

2.    22

3.    23

4.    24

5.    25

Count. Mark an X on the correct number of ice skates.

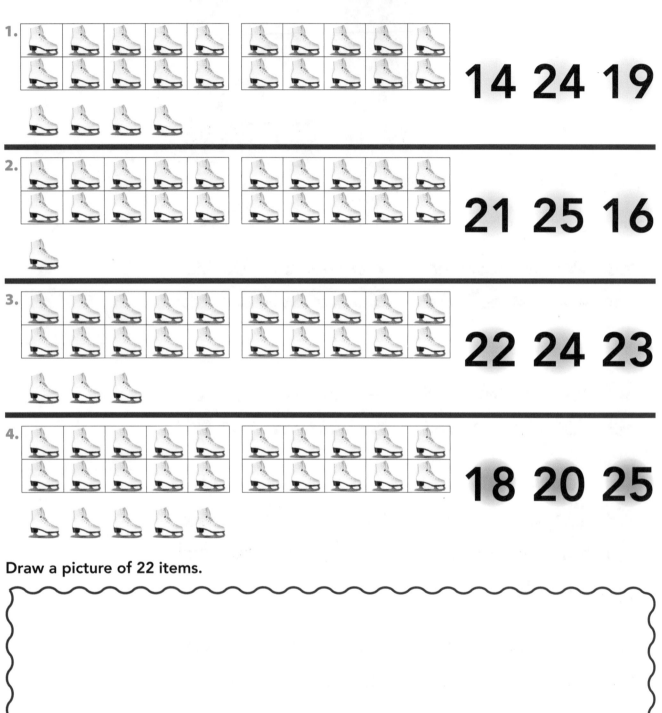

1. 14 24 19

2. 21 25 16

3. 22 24 23

4. 18 20 25

Draw a picture of 22 items.

Name _____

Count. Trace and write the numbers.

1.
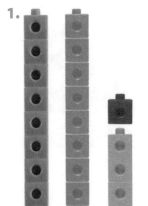

2.
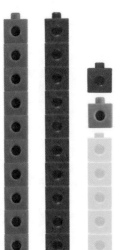

3.
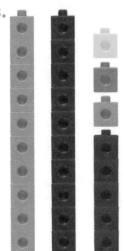

4.

5.
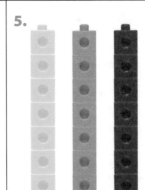

6.
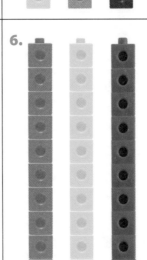

Write the missing numbers. Listen to your teacher and color.

December

Sunday	Monday	Tuesday	Wednesday	Thursday	Friday	Saturday
			1	2	3	4
5	_____	7	8	9	_____	11
12	13	_____	15	_____	17	18
19	_____	21	_____	23	_____	25
26	_____	28	29	_____	31	

Identify Numbers to 50

Count the balls. Trace the correct number.

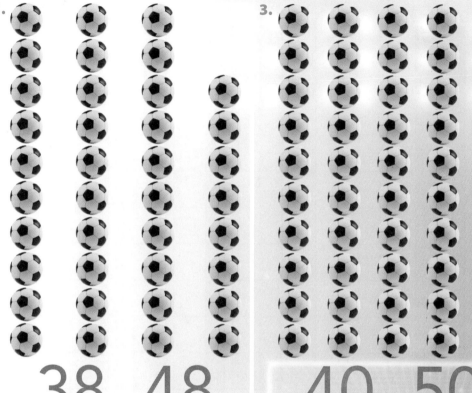

1.
38   48

3.
40   50

2.
45   46

4.
34   43

Color the spaces to match the number.

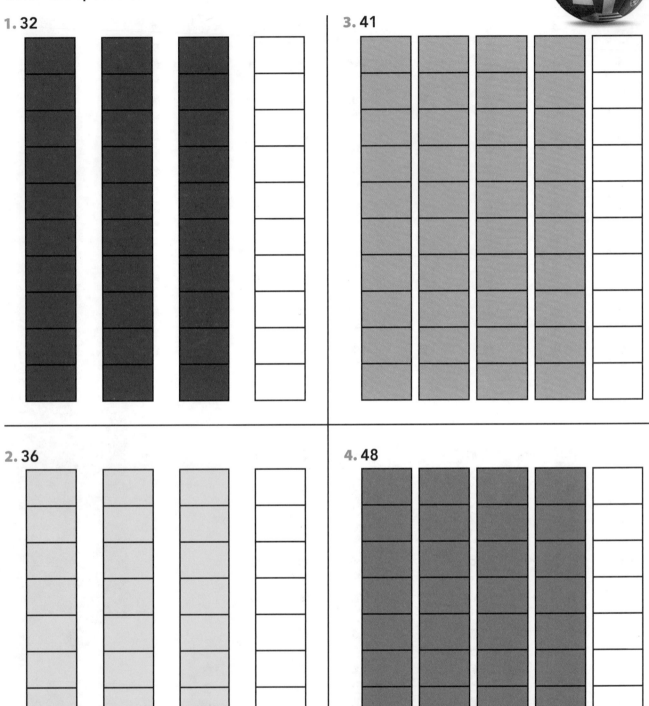

1. 32

2. 36

3. 41

4. 48

Name _____

Count the squares. Write the number.

1.
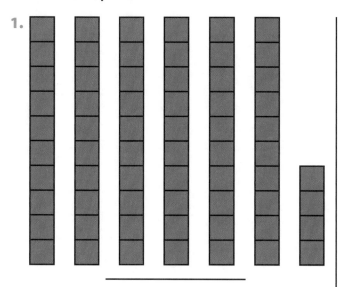

_____

- - - - - - - - - - - - - - - -

_____

3.
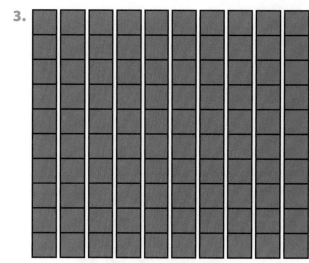

_____

- - - - - - - - - - - - - - - -

_____

2.
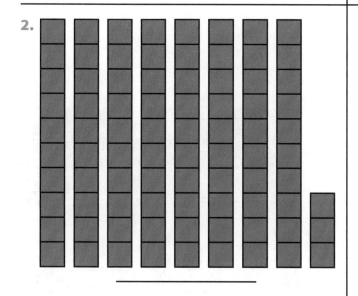

_____

- - - - - - - - - - - - - - - -

_____

4.
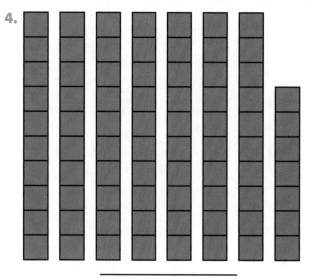

_____

- - - - - - - - - - - - - - - -

_____

Help Isabella follow the path home. Color the numbers from 80 to 100 in order.

80	81	82	27
30	72	83	84
88	87	86	85
89	90	91	55

23	96	95	94	93	92	14

31	97	64	44
56	98	99	100

Name _____

Hide the picture. Estimate. Then count and write the number.

1. Estimate.

Count.

2. Estimate.

Count.

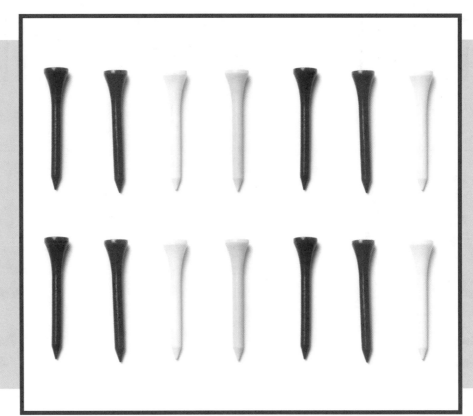

Look at the example. Estimate and fill in the circle.

1. more than

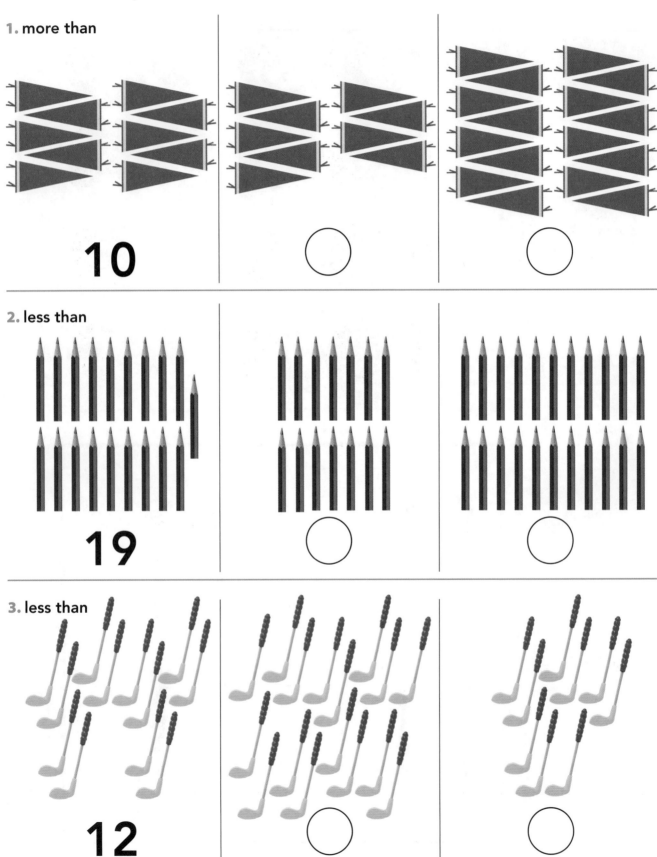

10

2. less than

19

3. less than

12

Name _____

Trace the lines. Count on. Circle the number where the ball will land.

1.

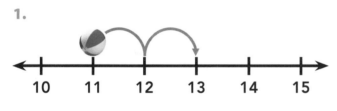

10   11   12   13   14   15

2.

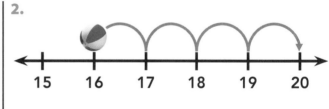

15   16   17   18   19   20

Count on 3. Draw lines. Circle the number where the ball will land.

3.

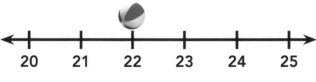

20   21   22   23   24   25

5.

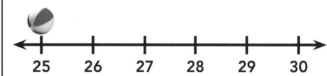

25   26   27   28   29   30

4.

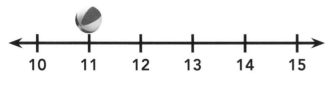

10   11   12   13   14   15

6.

20   21   22   23   24   25

© *Mathematics* Kindergarten

Trace the lines. Count back. Circle the number where the ball will land.

1.

14 15 16 17 18 19

2.

10 11 12 13 14 15

Count back 4. Draw lines. Circle the number where the ball will land.

3.

26 27 28 29 30 31

5.

11 12 13 14 15 16

4.

20 21 22 23 24 25

6.

25 26 27 28 29 30

Name _____

Read the graph of favorite sports. Complete the exercises.

1. Circle the sport that is the most favorite.

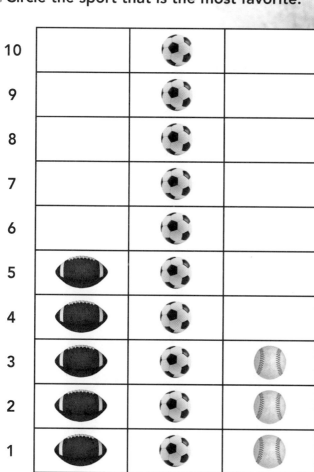

football   soccer   baseball

2. Mark an X on the least favorite.

3. Circle which is less.

or

4. Count and write how many balls in all.

_____

_____

Read the graph of favorite sports.

1. Circle the sport that is the most favorite.

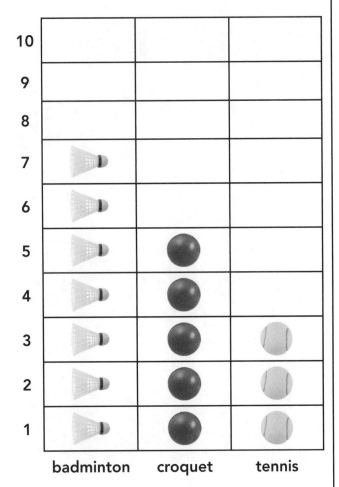

	badminton	croquet	tennis
10			
9			
8			
7	🏸		
6	🏸		
5	🏸	⚫	
4	🏸	⚫	
3	🏸	⚫	⚪
2	🏸	⚫	⚪
1	🏸	⚫	⚪

2. Mark an **X** on the least favorite.

---

3. Circle which is more.

or

Write how many more.

_____

- - - - - - - - - - - - - - -

_____

---

4. Count and write how many there are together.

 and

_____

- - - - - - - - - - - - - - -

_____

Name _____

Estimate. Fill in the circle.

1. more than

10

◯

◯

2. less than

18

◯

◯

Count. Circle the number.

3. 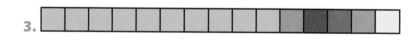 **10 12 15**

4. **16 19 20**

5. **15 17 18**

Count. Write the number.

1.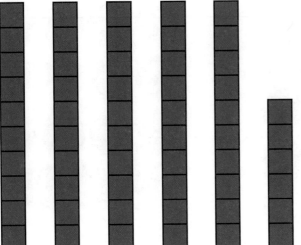

_____

- - - - - - - - - - - - - - - - - - - -

_____

2.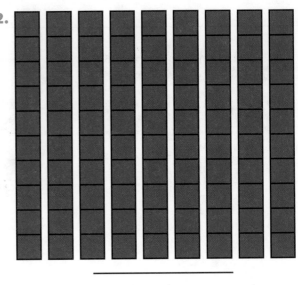

_____

- - - - - - - - - - - - - - - - - - - -

_____

3. Count on 4. Circle the number.

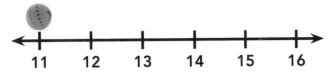

| 11 | 12 | 13 | 14 | 15 | 16 |

4. Count back 3. Circle the number.

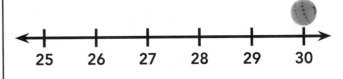

| 25 | 26 | 27 | 28 | 29 | 30 |

Write the missing numbers.

5.

20	21	- - - - - - - - - -	23	24
25	- - - - - - - - - -	27	28	29
- - - - - - - - - -	31	32	33	34

Estimate. Fill in the circle.

1. more than

 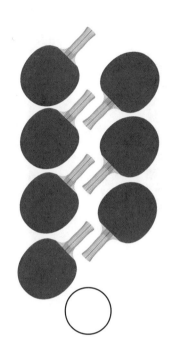 

6 ◯ ◯

2. less than

 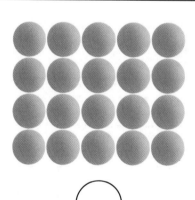

12 ◯ ◯

Count. Circle the number.

3.  **9 10 11**

4. **12 14 15**

5.  **11 13 16**

Count. Write the number.

1.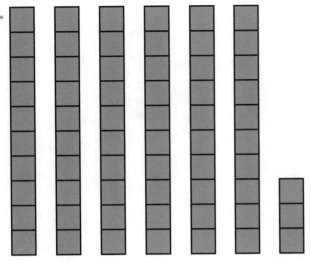

_____

- - - - - - - - - - - - - - - - - - - -

_____

2.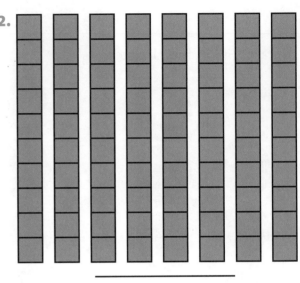

_____

- - - - - - - - - - - - - - - - - - - -

_____

3. **Count on 5. Circle the number.**

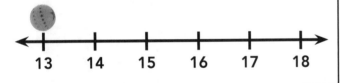

13   14   15   16   17   18

4. **Count back 2. Circle the number.**

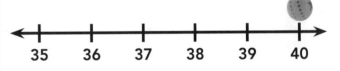

35   36   37   38   39   40

Write the missing numbers.

5.

10	11	12	------	14
15	------	17	18	19
------	21	22	23	24

Chapter 8
Count and Sequence

But everything should be done in
a fitting and orderly way.
1 Corinthians 14:40

Key Ideas:

Patterns: finding patterns in sequencing
of counting

Patterns: finding number patterns using
a hundred chart

Patterns: skip counting by 2s, 5s, and 10s

Number Theory: using ordinal numbers
first through tenth

Circle every set of matching butterflies. Count and write the number. Color.

MATH AT THE SCIENCE MUSEUM

Name _____

Trace over the gray lines to show two more or two less. Write the number.

1. more

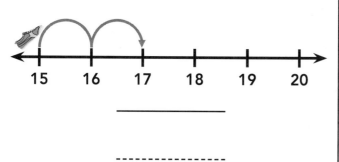

_____

- - - - - - - - - - -

_____

4. less

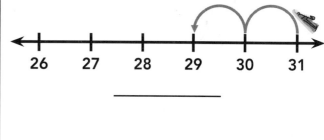

_____

- - - - - - - - - - -

_____

2. less

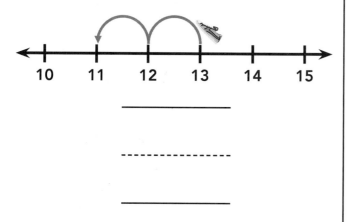

_____

- - - - - - - - - - -

_____

5. more

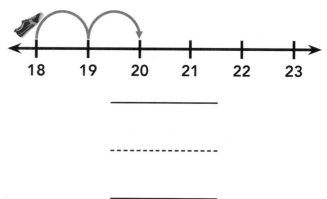

_____

- - - - - - - - - - -

_____

3. more

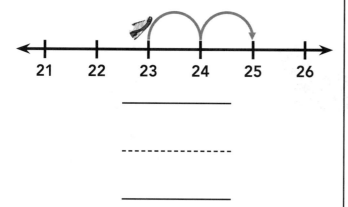

_____

- - - - - - - - - - -

_____

6. less

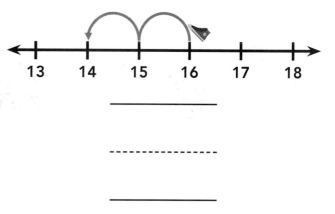

_____

- - - - - - - - - - -

_____

Count and write two more or two less.

1. more

19 ⟶ _____

2. less

_____ ⟵ 28

3. more

22 ⟶ _____

4. less

_____ ⟵ 17

1. Count by 2s and color those number rectangles blue.

1	2	3	4	5	6	7	8	9	10
11	12	13	14	15	16	17	18	19	20
21	22	23	24	25	26	27	28	29	30

2. Circle each set of 2. Count by 2s and write the number.

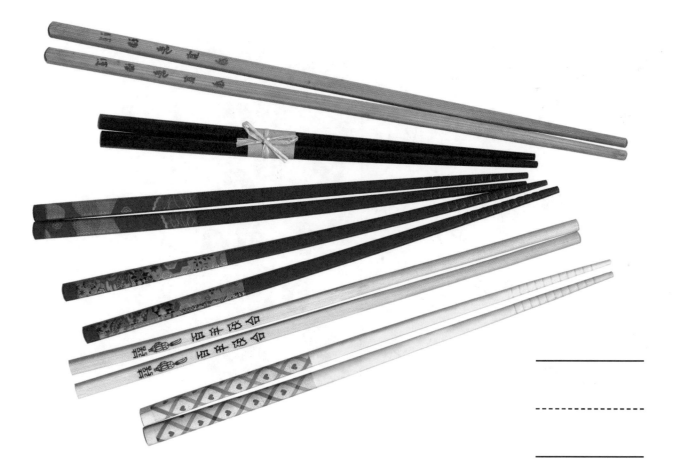

_____

- - - - - - - - - - - - - - -

_____

1. Skip count by 2s and circle each number.

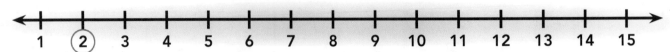

2. Write the circled numbers above in order.

3. Circle each group of 2. Count by 2s and write the number.

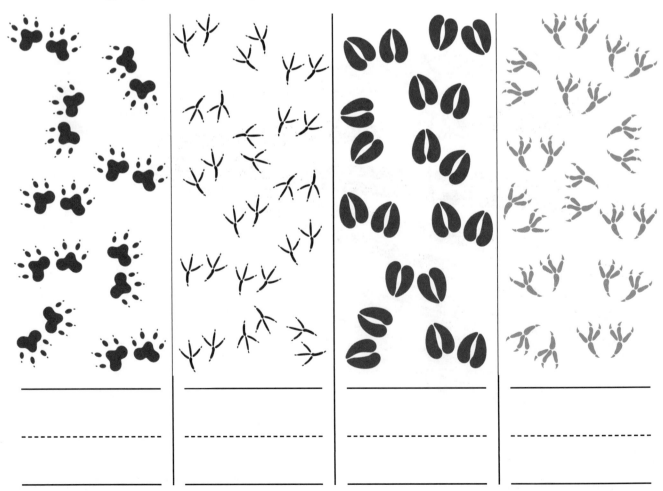

1. Count by 5s and color those number rectangles yellow.

1	2	3	4	5	6	7	8	9	10
11	12	13	14	15	16	17	18	19	20
21	22	23	24	25	26	27	28	29	30

2. Skip count by 5s and write the numbers.

_____   _____   _____

- - - - - - - - -   - - - - - - - - -   - - - - - - - - -

_____   _____   _____

- - - - - - - - -   - - - - - - - - -   - - - - - - - - -

_____   _____   _____

Count and circle the number of fingers.

3.

15 10 18

4.

21 25 20

1. Skip count by 5s and circle each number.

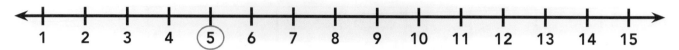

1 2 3 4 ⑤ 6 7 8 9 10 11 12 13 14 15

2. Draw five rocks in each space. Count by 5s and write the number.

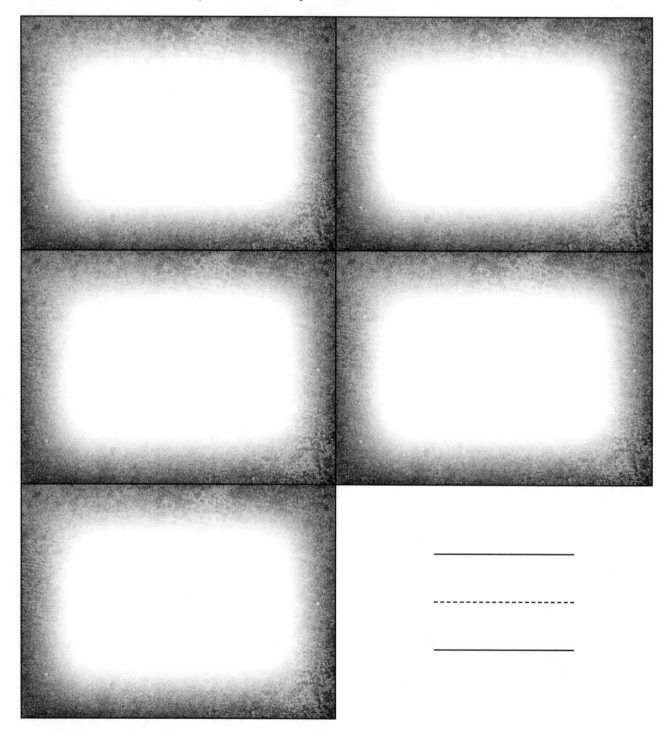

_____

- - - - - - - - - - - - - - - - -

_____

1. Count by 10s and color those number rectangles green.

1	2	3	4	5	6	7	8	9	10
11	12	13	14	15	16	17	18	19	20
21	22	23	24	25	26	27	28	29	30

2. Skip count by 10s and write the numbers.

————————————   ————————————   ————————————

- - - - - - - - - - - - - - -   - - - - - - - - - - - - - - -   - - - - - - - - - - - - - - -

————————————   ————————————   ————————————

3. Cut out and glue to match the fingers.

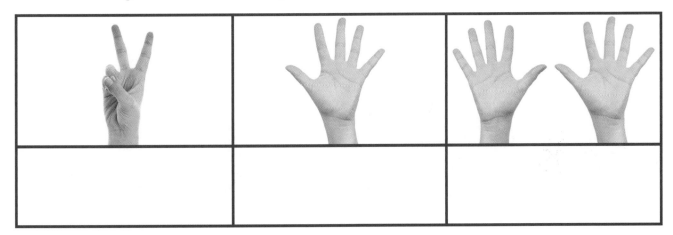

5 10 15 20 25   2 4 6 8 10   10 20 30

Count by 10s and connect the dots.

Name _____

Circle the picture that shows before.

Mark an X on the picture that shows after.

1.

2.

Draw what might happen after.

3.

before

after

Write 1, 2, and 3 to order the pictures.

1.

_____   _____   _____

- - - - - - - - - - - - - - -   - - - - - - - - - - - - - - -   - - - - - - - - - - - - - - -

_____   _____   _____

2.

_____   _____   _____

- - - - - - - - - - - - - - -   - - - - - - - - - - - - - - -   - - - - - - - - - - - - - - -

_____   _____   _____

Cut and glue the words in the correct order.

1.

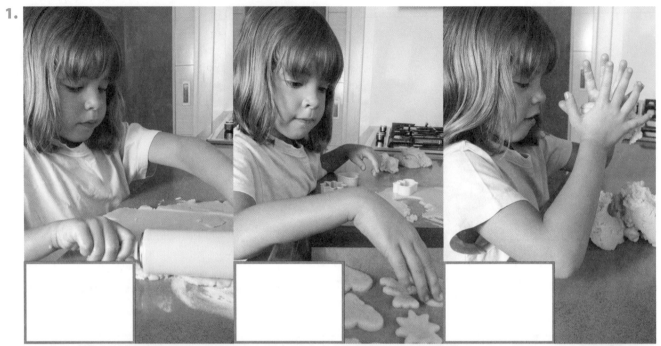

2.

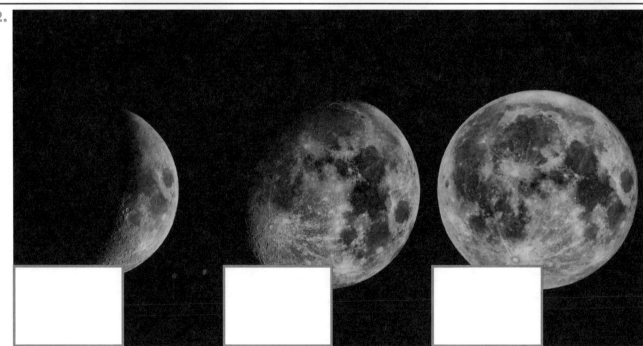

✂ ┈┈┈┈┈┈┈┈┈┈┈┈┈┈┈┈┈┈┈┈┈┈┈┈┈┈┈┈

first | next | last | first | next | last

1. Color the first rocket blue. Color the second rocket green. Color the third rocket red.

2. Draw second and third.

first
1st

second
2nd

third
3rd

Circle the number of the colored planet.

1.

1st 2nd 3rd

2.
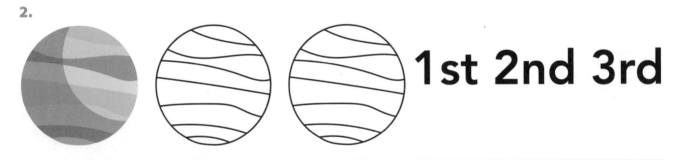

1st 2nd 3rd

3.
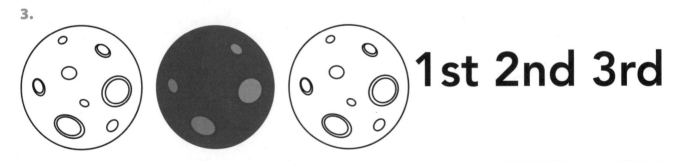

1st 2nd 3rd

4.
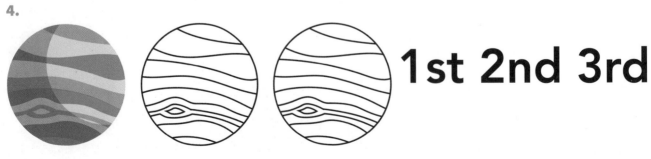

1st 2nd 3rd

Name _____

Ordinal Numbers: Fourth–Tenth 8.8

Circle the third planet. Mark an X on the seventh planet. Draw a line under the fifth

planet. Put a ☐ around the eighth planet.

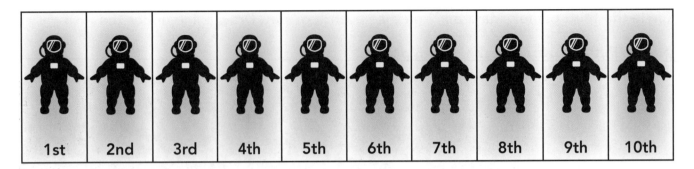

| 1st | 2nd | 3rd | 4th | 5th | 6th | 7th | 8th | 9th | 10th |

Color the item to match the number.

1. **8th** ☆ ☆ ☆ ☆ ☆ ☆ ☆ ☆ ☆ ☆

2. **2nd**

3. **5th**

4. **3rd**

5. **10th**

6. **1st**

Name _____

Circle the first in each set. Read the set in the correct order.

1. from left to right

4. from right to left

2. from top to bottom

5. from bottom to top

3. from left to right

6. from bottom to top

Color according to the directions.

1. Color the test tubes from left to right. Color them red, blue, and green.

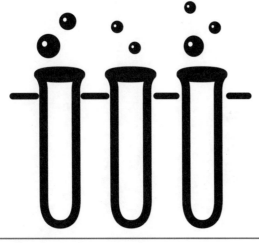

2. Color the magnets from top to bottom. Color them yellow, red, and orange.

3. Color the microscope from bottom to top. Color it black, yellow, and blue.

Name _____

Follow the directions.

1. Draw spots on the fish at the top left.

2. Draw stripes on the fish that are facing right.

3. Color the right column of fish. Color from top to bottom blue, orange, and yellow.

Follow the directions to draw a sunflower.

1 Draw a circle and a tall rectangle.

2 Draw triangles.

3 Add leaves.

1. Color the graph to match your class graph.

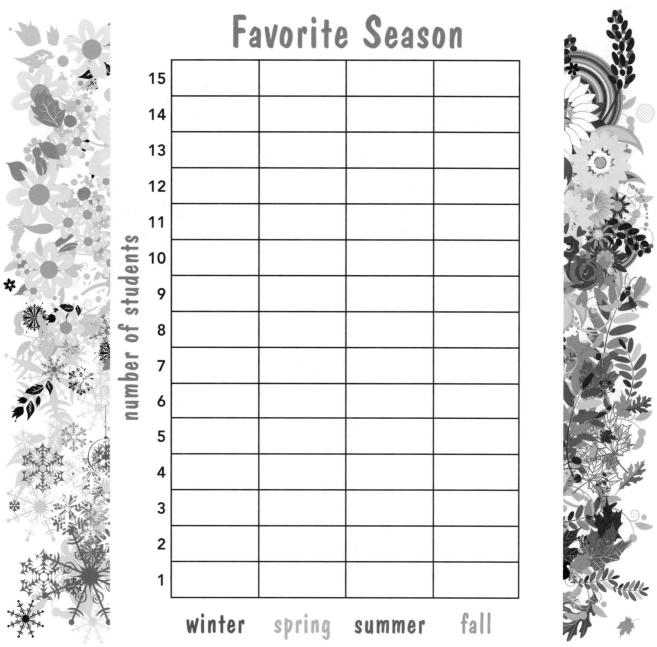

Favorite Season

number of students

	winter	spring	summer	fall
15				
14				
13				
12				
11				
10				
9				
8				
7				
6				
5				
4				
3				
2				
1				

Color the rectangles below blue, green, red, or orange to answer the questions.

2. Which season was your favorite?

3. Which season was the class favorite?

4. Which season was chosen by the fewest students?

Color the graph to match the number of children at the exhibits.

4						
3						
2						
1						

Name _____

Count and write 2 more or 2 less.

1. 2 less

_____

- - - - - - - - - - - - - - - -

_____

_____

2. 2 more

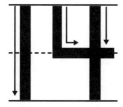      _____

- - - - - - - - - - - - - - - -

_____

Skip count. Circle the numbers.

3. 2s

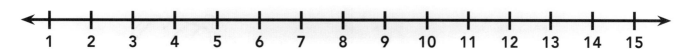

1 2 3 4 5 6 7 8 9 10 11 12 13 14 15

4. 5s

1 2 3 4 5 6 7 8 9 10 11 12 13 14 15

5. 10s

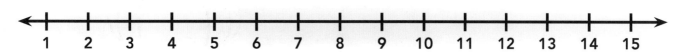

1 2 3 4 5 6 7 8 9 10 11 12 13 14 15

Circle.

1. before

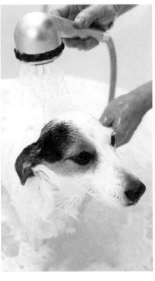

2. last

3. second

Color red, yellow, and green.

4. from right to left

5. from bottom to top

Name _____

1. Write the number that is 2 more.

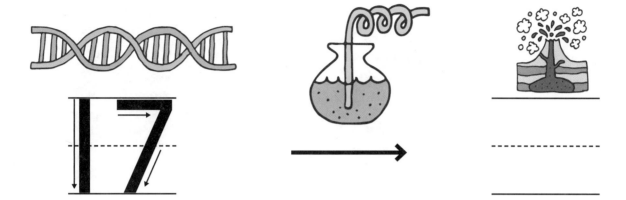

17 →

_____

_____

2. Skip count and color by 2s.

1	2	3	4	5	6	7	8	9	10
11	12	13	14	15	16	17	18	19	20

3. Skip count and color by 5s.

1	2	3	4	5	6	7	8	9	10
11	12	13	14	15	16	17	18	19	20

4. Skip count and color by 10s.

1	2	3	4	5	6	7	8	9	10
11	12	13	14	15	16	17	18	19	20

Mark an X.

1. after

2. first

3. third

Color blue, orange, and black.

4. from left to right

5. from top to bottom

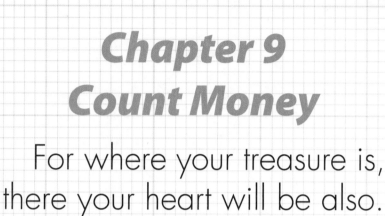

Chapter 9
Count Money

For where your treasure is,
there your heart will be also.
Matthew 6:21

Key Ideas:

Money: recognizing and counting pennies,
nickels, and dimes

Money: recognizing and counting quarters

Money: recognizing one dollar and identifying
amounts equal to one dollar

Money: making buying decisions

Use the key to color the coins.

MATH AT THE FAIR

Key

Name _____

Circle the matching coins.

1. penny

3. dime

2. nickel

4. quarter

Cut and glue the coins on the correct bank.

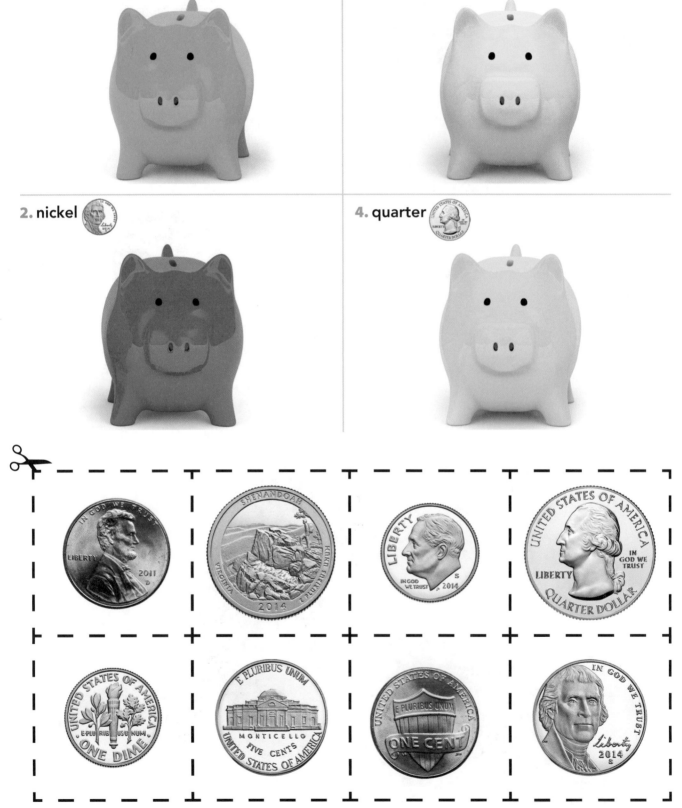

1. penny

2. nickel

3. dime

4. quarter

Name _____

Count the pennies and write the amount.

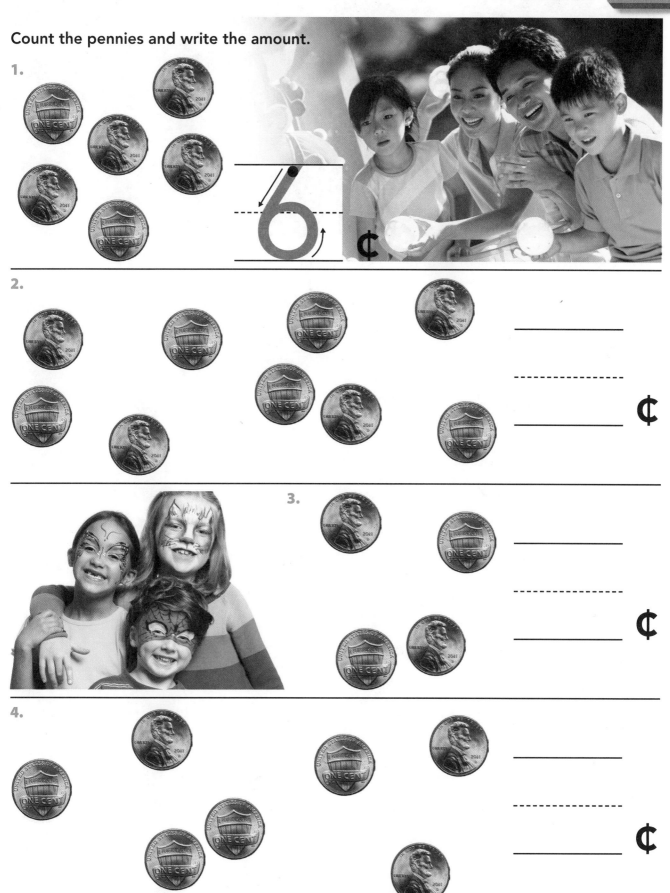

1.

6 ¢

2.

_____
_ _ _ _ _ _ _ _ _ _
_____ ¢

3.

_____
_ _ _ _ _ _ _ _ _ _
_____ ¢

4.

_____
_ _ _ _ _ _ _ _ _ _
_____ ¢

Circle the correct number of pennies to buy the tickets.

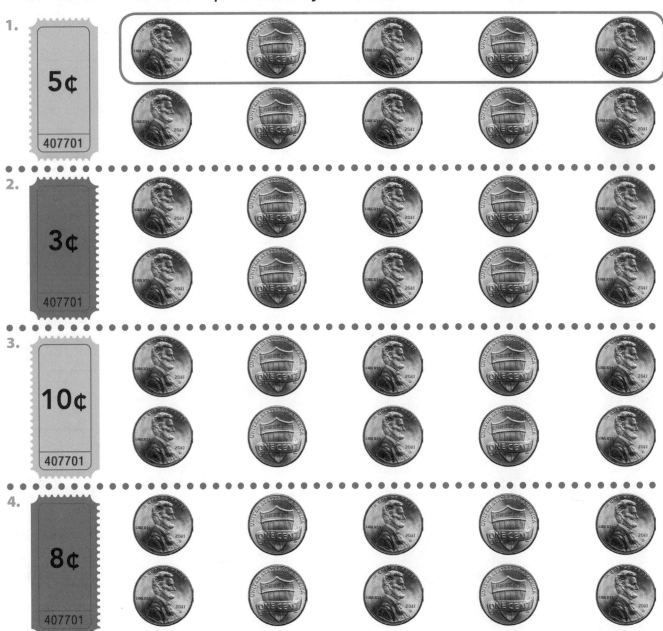

1. **5¢** 407701

2. **3¢** 407701

3. **10¢** 407701

4. **8¢** 407701

Name _____

Count by 5s and write the value.

1.

_____

_____ ¢

2.

_____

_____ ¢

3.

_____

_____ ¢

Count by 5s and circle the correct amount of money.

4.

20¢ 23¢ 30¢

5.

17¢ 20¢ 25¢

Draw lines to match the nickels to the prices.

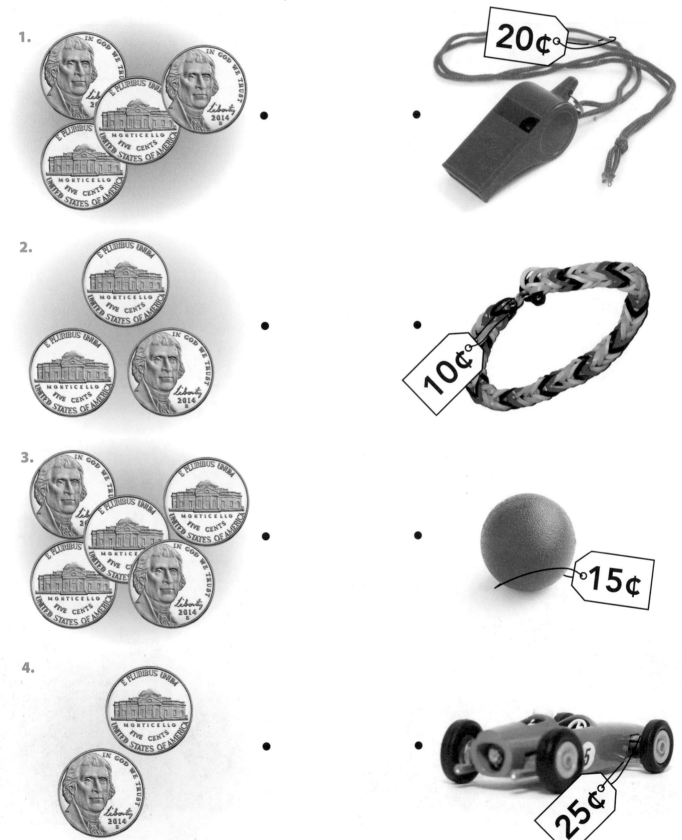

1.

2.

3.

4.

Name _____

Count by 10s and write the value.

1.

¢

2.

¢

3.

¢

4.

¢

Circle the correct number of dimes to buy each item.

1. 30¢

2. 40¢

3. 10¢

4. 20¢

Name _____

Count on and write the amount.

1.

_____
- - - - - - - - - - - - - - - -
_____ ¢

2.

_____
- - - - - - - - - - - - - - - -
_____ ¢

3.

_____
- - - - - - - - - - - - - - - -
_____ ¢

4.

_____
- - - - - - - - - - - - - - - -
_____ ¢

5.

_____
- - - - - - - - - - - - - - - -
_____ ¢

Draw lines to match the coins to the prices.

1.

  •

• **22¢**

2.

    •

• **25¢**

3.

   •

• **11¢**

Color the coins that make the amount.

4. •15¢

5. •25¢

Name _____

Count on and trace the amounts.

1.

25 ¢

2.

50 ¢

3.

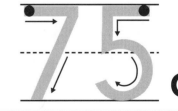 ¢

4.

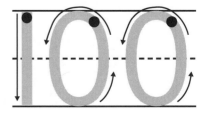 ¢

Draw a path through the ride by following the quarters.

Name _____

Cut and match the coins to make an even trade for a dollar. Glue the coins on the dollar.

1.

3.

2.

4.

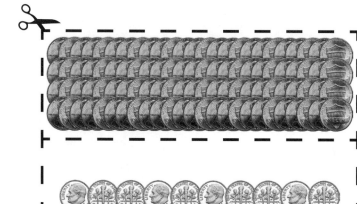

Mark an **X** on the dimes to make an even trade for a dollar.
Circle the quarters to make an even trade for a dollar.

Compare Values 9.8

Write the amount of money in each set. Circle the amount that is more.

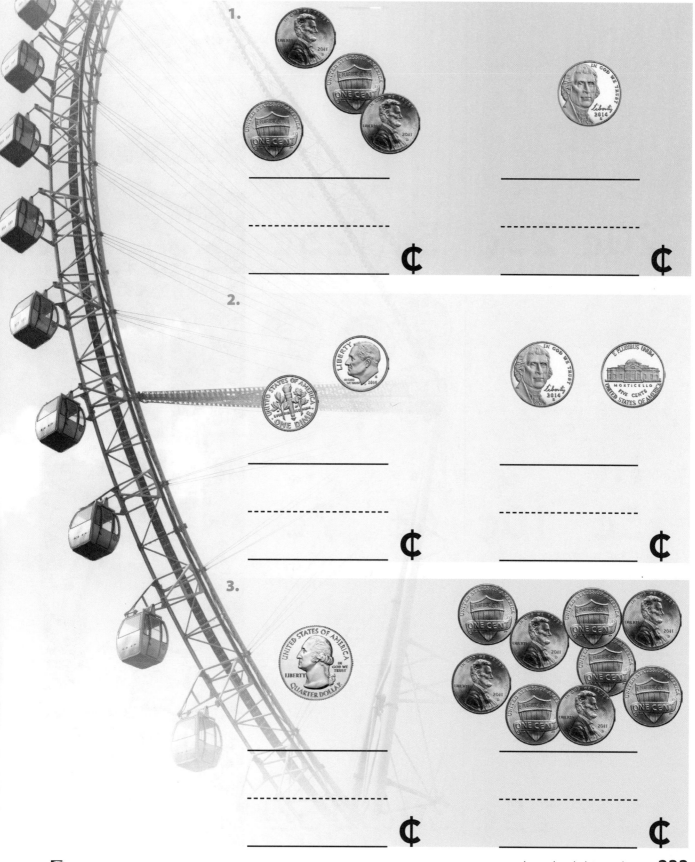

1.

_____   _____

- - - - - - - - - - - -   - - - - - - - - - - - -

¢   ¢

2.

_____   _____

- - - - - - - - - - - -   - - - - - - - - - - - -

¢   ¢

3.

_____   _____

- - - - - - - - - - - -   - - - - - - - - - - - -

¢   ¢

Draw lines to match the coins to the amount. Mark an X on the amount that is less.

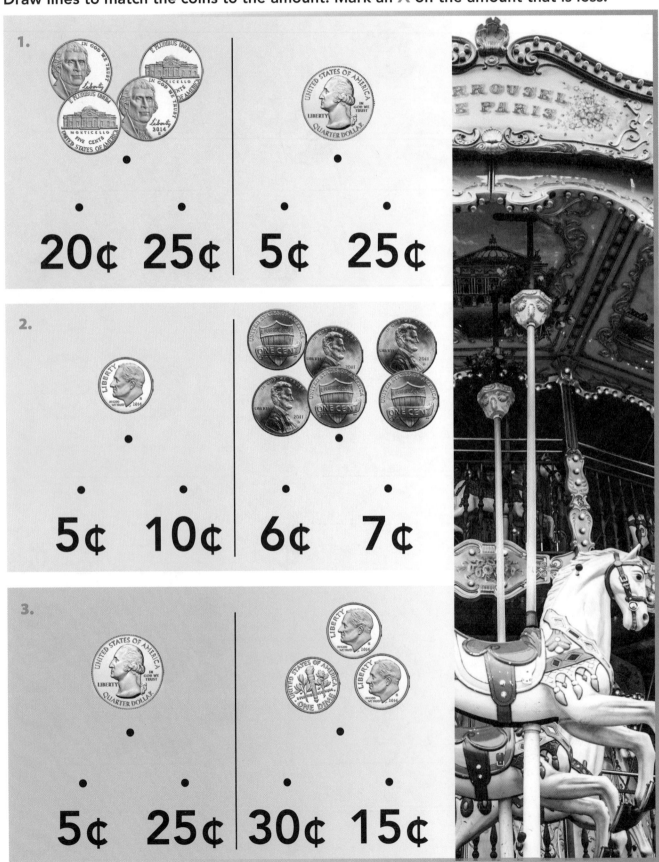

1. 20¢   25¢ | 5¢   25¢

2. 5¢   10¢ | 6¢   7¢

3. 5¢   25¢ | 30¢   15¢

Count on and write the amount of money.

1.   _____

_ _ _ _ _ _ _ _ _ _ _ _ _ _ _ _

_____ **¢**

2.   _____

_ _ _ _ _ _ _ _ _ _ _ _ _ _ _ _

_____ **¢**

3.   _____

_ _ _ _ _ _ _ _ _ _ _ _ _ _ _ _

_____ **¢**

4.   _____

_ _ _ _ _ _ _ _ _ _ _ _ _ _ _ _

_____ **¢**

5.   _____

_ _ _ _ _ _ _ _ _ _ _ _ _ _ _ _

_____ **¢**

6.   _____

_ _ _ _ _ _ _ _ _ _ _ _ _ _ _ _

_____ **¢**

Count how much for each item. Color in the circle.

1.

○ **5¢**
○ **12¢**
○ **13¢**

2.

○ **15¢**
○ **16¢**
○ **11¢**

3.

○ **21¢**
○ **28¢**
○ **30¢**

4.

○ **25¢**
○ **20¢**
○ **15¢**

5.

○ **17¢**
○ **37¢**
○ **27¢**

Count on and write the amount of money on the blank. Circle the amount that is more.

1.

_____

- - - - - - - - - - - - - - - - - -

_____ ¢

_____

- - - - - - - - - - - - - - - - - -

_____ ¢

2.

_____

- - - - - - - - - - - - - - - - - -

_____ ¢

_____

- - - - - - - - - - - - - - - - - -

_____ ¢

Count on and write the amount of money on the first blank. Cut and glue the coins to make more or less. Count on and write that amount of money on the second blank.

1. more

_____

- - - - - - - - - - - - - - - - - -

_____ ¢

_____

- - - - - - - - - - - - - - - - - -

_____ ¢

2. less

_____

- - - - - - - - - - - - - - - - - -

_____ ¢

_____

- - - - - - - - - - - - - - - - - -

_____ ¢

Read the picture graph and match the amounts.

Money for Missions Day

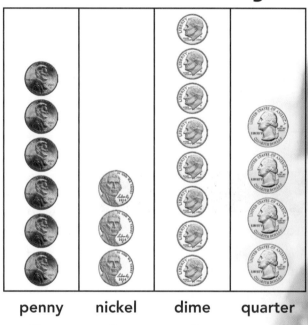

penny	nickel	dime	quarter
•	•	•	•

1. • 15¢   • $1.00   • 6¢   • 80¢

_____

- - - - - - - - - - - - - - - - -

2. How many ? _____

3. Circle the coin there is more of.   or

1. Make a bar graph. Color the number of rectangles for each amount shown.

Amusement Park

number of items

5 4 3 2 1

10¢   25¢ $1.00

money

Read the graph and circle the correct price.

2. most sold

10¢   25¢ $1.00

3. least sold

10¢   25¢ $1.00

Color in the circle that shows the value of the coin.

1.

○ **1¢**
○ **5¢**
○ **10¢**

2.

○ **1¢**
○ **5¢**
○ **10¢**

Circle the correct number of coins to match the price.

3.
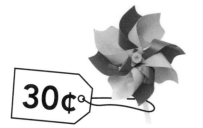
30¢

4.
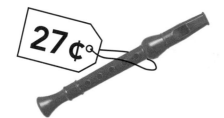
27¢

Draw lines to match the coins and the price tags.

5.

•   •

20¢

6.

•   •

$1.00

Compare value. Mark an X on the set.

1. more

---

2. less

●●

Count on and write the amount of money.

3.

_____
- - - - - - - - - - - - - - - - - - - -
_____ ¢

4.

_____
- - - - - - - - - - - - - - - - - - - -
_____ ¢

5.

_____
- - - - - - - - - - - - - - - - - - - -
_____ ¢

●●

Circle the coin on the right that is the same value as the pennies.

6.

Draw lines to match the coin to its value.

1.

· **5¢**
· **10¢**
· **25¢**

2.

· **5¢**
· **10¢**
· **25¢**

Circle the coins to match the price.

3.
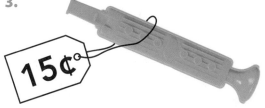
15¢

4.

$1.00

Count on and fill in the circle.

5.

○ **32¢**
○ **22¢**
○ **12¢**

6.

○ **32¢**
○ **22¢**
○ **12¢**

Circle the coin on the right that is the same value as the set.

1.

 |

2.

     |

Count on and compare the values. Circle the correct set.

3. more

4. less

Chapter 10
Telling Time

Trust in Him at all times.
Psalm 62:8a

Key Ideas:

Time: telling time to the hour

Time: telling time to the half hour

Time: reading a schedule

Write the missing numbers.

Write the time.

1.

____ **o'clock**

2.

____ **o'clock**

3.

____ **o'clock**

4.

____ **o'clock**

5.

____ **o'clock**

6.

____ **o'clock**

Draw the hour hand.

1.

6 o'clock

4.

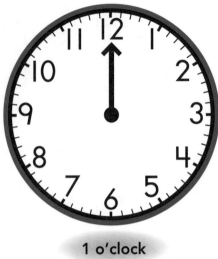

1 o'clock

2.

3 o'clock

5.

5 o'clock

3.

10 o'clock

6.

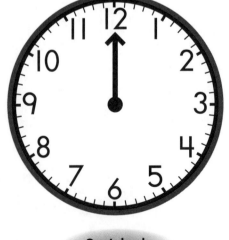

9 o'clock

Name _____

Write the number.

1.

 **2** o'clock

4.

_____ o'clock

2.

_____ o'clock

5.

_____ o'clock

3.

_____ o'clock

6.

_____ o'clock

© *Mathematics* Kindergarten

two hundred forty-nine **249**

Draw lines to match the times.

1.

•

2.

•

•

3.

•

•

4.

•

•

•

Read the time. Circle the hour hand. Draw the minute hand.

1.

1:30

4.

7:30

2.

3:30

5.

12:30

3.

10:30

6.

5:30

Circle the clock that shows the correct time.

1. 2:30

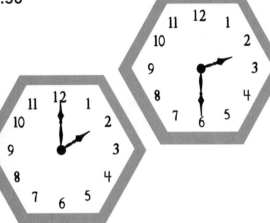

3. 4:30

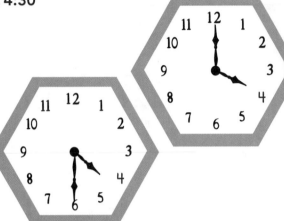

2. 9:30

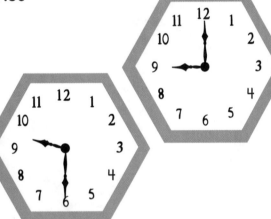

4. 6:30

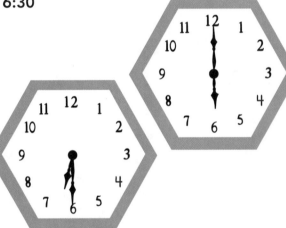

Draw the hour and minute hands.

5.

11:30

6.

8:30

Name _____

Read the clock and write the time.

Circle the matching digital time.

1.

3. Color the hour times :00 blue. Color the half-hour times :30 yellow.

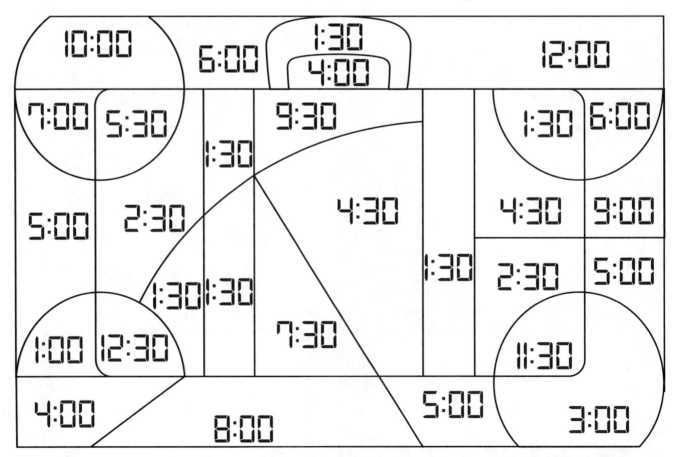

Draw or write the correct time.

1.

7:00

2.

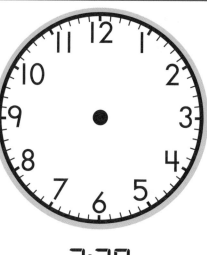

3:30

4.

■

- -

■

3.

8:00

5.

■

- -

■

Write the digital times.

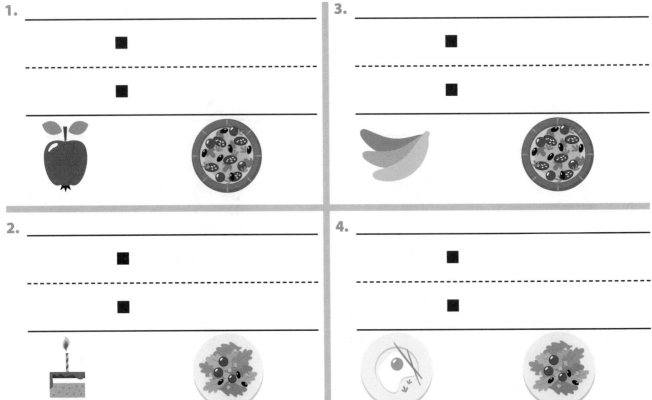

1. _____
   ■
   - - - - - - - - - -
   ■
   _____

2. _____
   ■
   - - - - - - - - - -
   ■
   _____

3. _____
   ■
   - - - - - - - - - -
   ■
   _____

4. _____
   ■
   - - - - - - - - - -
   ■
   _____

Name _____

Draw lines to match the event to the time of day.

1. morning

•   •

2. afternoon

•   •

3. evening

•   •

Circle the word that tells when the event happens.

1.

☀ **morning**

☀ **afternoon**

🌙 **evening**

2.

☀ **morning**

☀ **afternoon**

🌙 **evening**

3.

☀ **morning**

☀ **afternoon**

🌙 **evening**

4.

☀ **morning**

☀ **afternoon**

🌙 **evening**

Name _____

Look at the class schedule. Number the pictures 1, 2, and 3 in order.

CLASS SCHEDULE

🔭 8:00 Science

✏️ 9:00 Writing

💻 10:00 Computers

1. 10:00 💻

2. 8:00 🔭

3. 9:00 ✏️

Look at the pictures about evening events. Draw a picture to complete the order.

1.

2.

Circle the picture that takes less time.

1.

2.

3.

Mark an X on the picture that takes more time.

Name _____

Fill in the missing hours. Draw the hour hand or write the number.

1.

_____

- - - - - - - - - - - - - - - - -

2. _____:00

3.

_____   _____

- - - - - - - - - - - - - - - -   - - - - - - - - - - - - - - - -

4. _____:00      _____:00

5.

Draw the hour hand.

1. Count on 1 hour.

2. Count on 2 hours.

3. Count back 1 hour.

4. Count back 2 hours.

Listen to the teacher and complete the graph.

South Christian School Math Times

5				
4				
3				
2				
1				

Circle the correct times.

1. most   9:00   9:30   3. more   9:30   10:30

2. least   9:30   10:30   4. less   9:00   10:00

Look at Ethan's schedule. Fill in the graph.

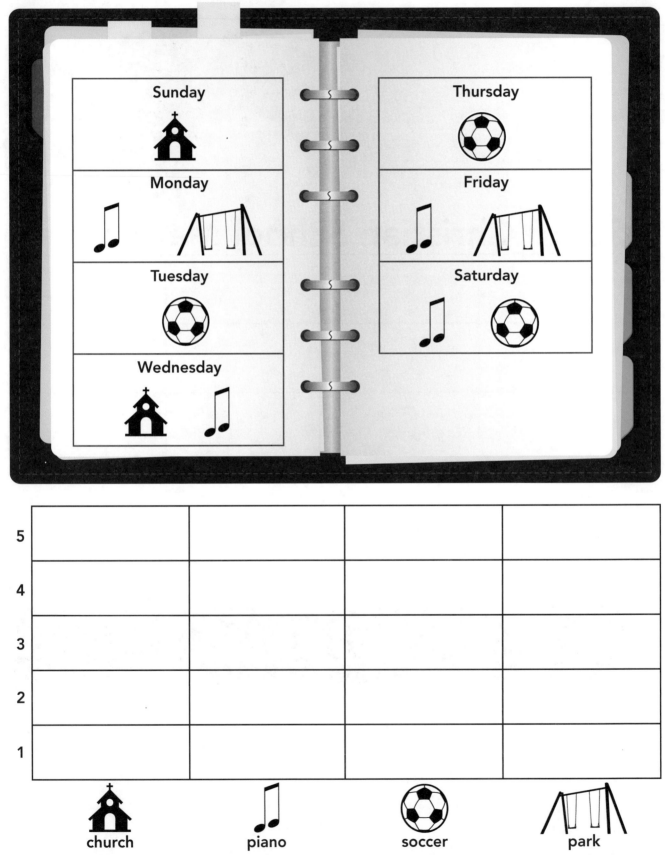

Name _____

Draw a line to match the times.

1.  •

2.  •

3.  •

4. Draw the hour hand on the clock below.

Write the missing times.

_____

- - - - - - - - - - - - - - - -

5. 3:00　　　4:00　　　_____:00

_____　　　_____

- - - - - - - - - - - - - - - -　　　- - - - - - - - - - - - - - - -

6. _____:30　　7:30　　_____:30

Label the pictures 1, 2, and 3 according to the times.

1. Reading

_____

- - - - - - - - - - - - - - - -

_____

2. Math

_____

- - - - - - - - - - - - - - - -

_____

3. Social Studies

_____

- - - - - - - - - - - - - - - -

_____

4. Draw something that takes more time to do.

Name _____

Circle the correct digital time.

1.

2.

3. Look at the clock. Write the time.

_____

- - - - - - - -

_____ o'clock

Fill in the missing times.

_____

- - - - - - - - - - - - - - -

4. _____:30   3:30   4:30

_____

- - - - - - - - - - - - - - -

5. 11:00   12:00   _____:00

Look at the times on the watches. Label the pictures 1, 2, and 3.

1. dinner _____
   _ _ _ _ _ _ _ _ _ _ _ _ _

2. homework _____
   _ _ _ _ _ _ _ _ _ _ _ _ _

3. violin _____
   _ _ _ _ _ _ _ _ _ _ _ _ _

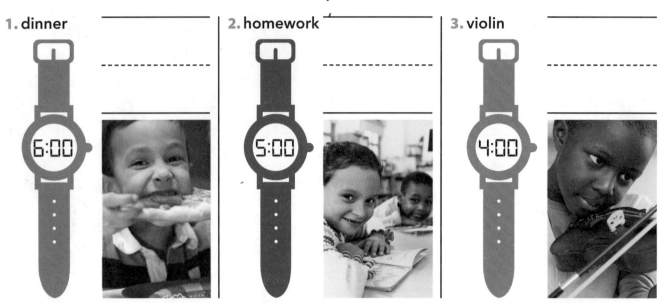

Circle the picture that took less time to do.

4.

5.

Chapter 11
Discover Addition

God made the wild animals according
to their kinds, the livestock according to their
kinds, and all the creatures that move along
the ground according to their kinds.
And God saw that it was good.
Genesis 1:25

Key Ideas:

Addition: adding sums to 10

Addition: using a number line for counting on

Algebra: writing number sentences

Algebra: finding missing addends

Count the animals in all. Write the number.

MATH AT THE ZOO

4 + 2 = _____

Count how many children in all. Circle the number.

1.

2 3 4

2.

2 3 4

3.

2 3 4

Count how many animals in all. Circle the number.

1.

3 4 5

2.

3 4 5

3.

3 4 5

Count. Write how many.

1.

_____

_____

_____

_____

How many in all?

_____

_____

2.

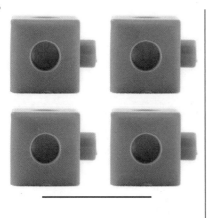

_____

_____

_____

_____

How many in all?

_____

_____

Count. Write how many.

1.

_____   _____   **How many in all?**
                                         _____

-----------------   -----------------   -----------------

_____   _____   _____

2.

_____   _____   **How many in all?**
                                         _____

-----------------   -----------------   -----------------

_____   _____   _____

3.

_____   _____   **How many in all?**
                                         _____

-----------------   -----------------   -----------------

_____   _____   _____

4.

_____   _____   **How many in all?**
                                         _____

-----------------   -----------------   -----------------

_____   _____   _____

Draw the picture for each number sentence. Write how many in all.

1 and 3 is _____.

2 and 1 is _____.

Draw the picture for each number sentence. Write how many in all.

1.

_____

2 and 2 is _____.

2.

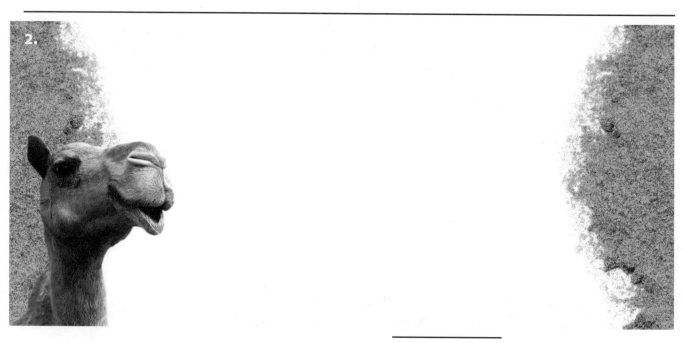

_____

2 and 3 is _____.

Write the number sentences.

1.

_____   _____   _____

---------------- + ---------------- = ----------------

2.

_____   _____   _____

---------------- + ---------------- = ----------------

3.

_____   _____   _____

---------------- + ---------------- = ----------------

Add the numbers. Color the carrot with the correct number.

1.

$$1 + 0 =$$

4.

$$3 + 2 =$$

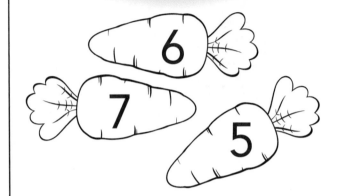

2.

$$2 + 1 =$$

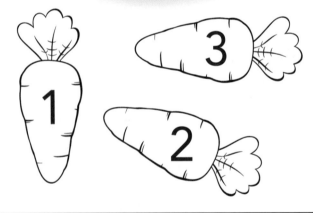

5.

$$5 + 0 =$$

3.

$$4 + 1 =$$

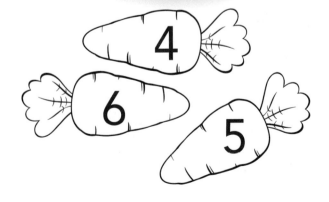

6.

$$1 + 3 =$$

Complete each addition problem.

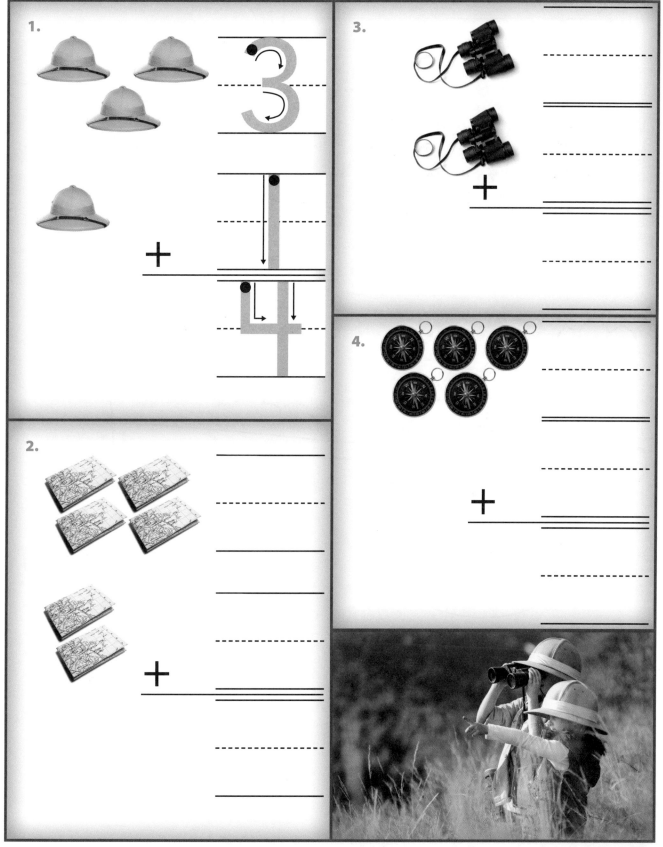

1.

2.

3.

4.

Add. Use the key to color the answers.

Key
1   2   3   4   5

$$\begin{array}{r} 2 \\ +\ 3 \\ \hline \end{array}$$

$$\begin{array}{r} 2 \\ +\ 1 \\ \hline \end{array}$$

$$1 + 3$$

$$2 + 2$$

$$0 + 2$$

$$1 + 1$$

$$\begin{array}{r} 1 \\ +\ 0 \\ \hline \end{array}$$

$$0 + 1$$

$$\begin{array}{r} 0 \\ +\ 1 \\ \hline \end{array}$$

$$\begin{array}{r} 1 \\ +\ 1 \\ \hline \end{array}$$

$$5 + 0$$

Color the circles. Write number sentences that equal 6.

1.

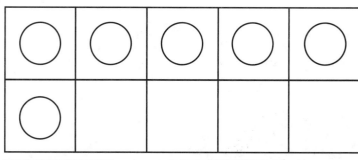

_____ + _____ = 6

2.

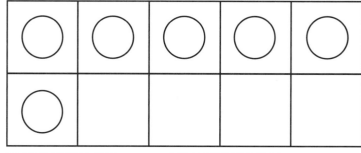

_____ + _____ = 6

3.

_____ + _____ = 6

Color the path of numbers that equal 6.

4 + 2	6 + 0			
3 + 3	2 + 0			
2 + 4	1 + 1	2 + 3	3 + 0	1 + 4
0 + 6	2 + 4	6 + 0	4 + 1	2 + 2
1 + 0	2 + 2	4 + 2	1 + 1	1 + 3
0 + 5	4 + 1	3 + 3	0 + 0	0 + 2
2 + 2	1 + 4	6 + 0		
3 + 2	0 + 0	5 + 1		
1 + 2	4 + 0	3 + 3		

Draw a picture of each story your teacher tells. Write the number sentence.

1. _____   _____   _____

    - - - - - - - - -   **+**   - - - - - - - - -   **=**   - - - - - - - - -

    _____   _____   _____

2. _____   _____   _____

    - - - - - - - - -   **+**   - - - - - - - - -   **=**   - - - - - - - - -

    _____   _____   _____

Draw a picture of each story your teacher tells. Write the number sentence.

1. _____   _____   _____

   ---------------- **+** ---------------- **=** ----------------

   _____   _____   _____

2. _____   _____   _____

   ---------------- **+** ---------------- **=** ----------------

   _____   _____   _____

Count on. Write the number sentence.

1.

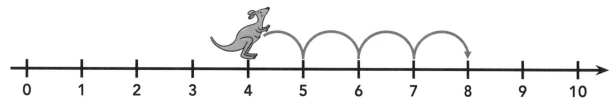

start	count on	stop
- - - - - - - - - **+** - - - - - - - - - **=** - - - - - - - - -

2.

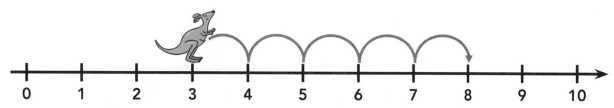

start	count on	stop
- - - - - - - - - **+** - - - - - - - - - **=** - - - - - - - - -

3.

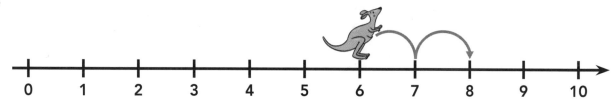

start	count on	stop
- - - - - - - - - **+** - - - - - - - - - **=** - - - - - - - - -

Fill in the circle beside the matching number sentence.

1.

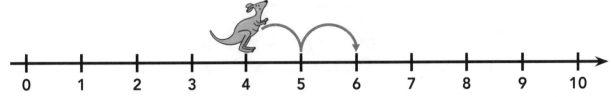

○ 2 + 3 = 5   ○ 4 + 2 = 6

2.

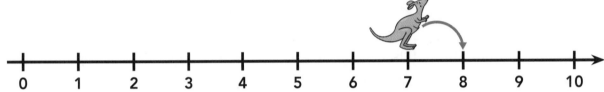

○ 7 + 1 = 8   ○ 4 + 4 = 8

3.

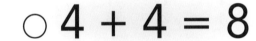

○ 2 + 5 = 7   ○ 3 + 4 = 7

4.

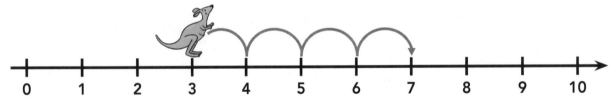

○ 2 + 5 = 7   ○ 5 + 3 = 8

Name _____

Estimate. Write the addition fact.

1.

Estimate.

_____
- - - - - - - - - - - - -
_____

$$\overset{2}{\underline{\hspace{2cm}}} + \overset{5}{\underline{\hspace{2cm}}} = \overset{7}{\underline{\hspace{2cm}}}$$

2.

   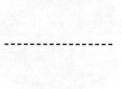

Estimate.

_____
- - - - - - - - - - - - -
_____

_____ + _____ = _____

- - - - - - -   - - - - - - -   - - - - - - -

_____   _____   _____

3.

Estimate.

_____
- - - - - - - - - - - - -
_____

_____ + _____ = _____

- - - - - - -   - - - - - - -   - - - - - - -

_____   _____   _____

Estimate. Write the addition fact.

1.

Estimate.

_____

- - - - - - - - - - - - - - -

_____

_____ + _____ = _____

2.

Estimate.

_____

- - - - - - - - - - - - - - -

_____

_____ + _____ = _____

3.

Estimate.

_____

- - - - - - - - - - - - - - -

_____

_____ + _____ = _____

Cut. Count and glue on the missing part. Write the parts that make the whole.

1.

_____   _____

------------ + ------------ = 10

_____   _____

2.

_____   _____

------------ + ------------ = 10

_____   _____

3.

_____   _____

------------ + ------------ = 10

_____   _____

4.

_____   _____

------------ + ------------ = 10

_____   _____

Count and draw more peanuts. Write the missing numbers.

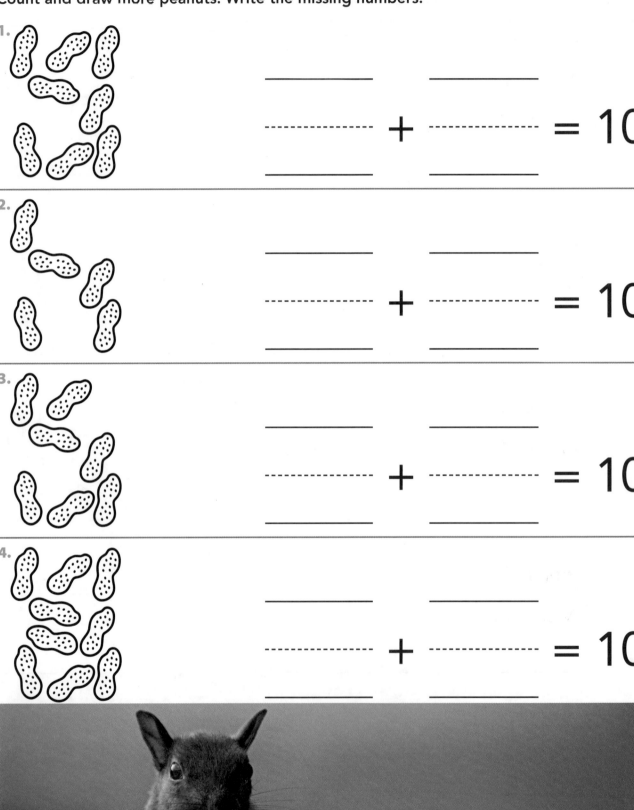

1.

_____ _____

------------- + ------------- = 10

_____ _____

2.

_____ _____

------------- + ------------- = 10

_____ _____

3.

_____ _____

------------- + ------------- = 10

_____ _____

4.

_____ _____

------------- + ------------- = 10

_____ _____

Name _____

Read the bar graph. Fill in the correct circle.

Favorite Pet

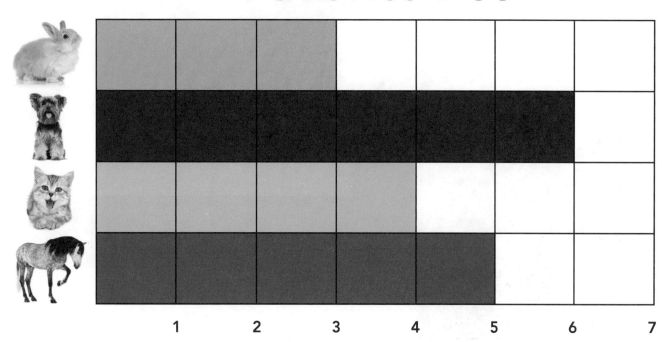

1. Which pet is liked by the most children?

2. Which pet is liked by the fewest children?

3. How many children chose and ?

 3   **4**   ○ **9**   ○ **6**

Read the bar graph. Write the number.

Safari Animals

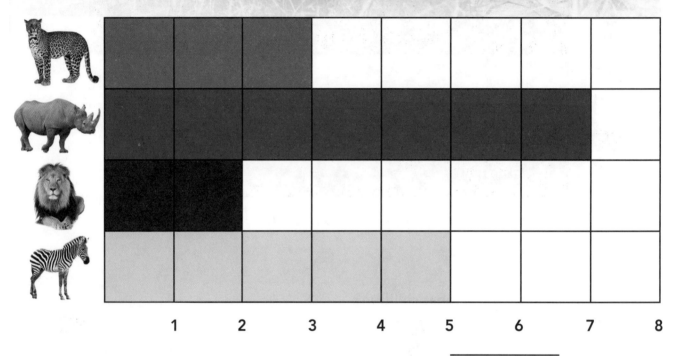

	1	2	3	4	5	6	7	8

_____

1. How many children chose ___ and ___ ? _____
_____

2. How many children chose ___ and ___ ? _____
_____

3. How many children chose ___ and ___ ? _____

Name _____

1. Fill in the blank.

How many in all?

_____

_____

Draw and answer.

2.

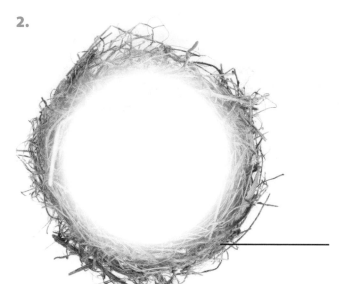

3.

_____

----

2 and 1 is _____. 4 and 0 is _____.

Write the addition facts.

4.

_____ _____ _____

---------- + ---------- = ----------

_____ _____ _____

5.

_____ _____ _____

---------- + ---------- = ----------

_____ _____ _____

1. Write the addition fact.

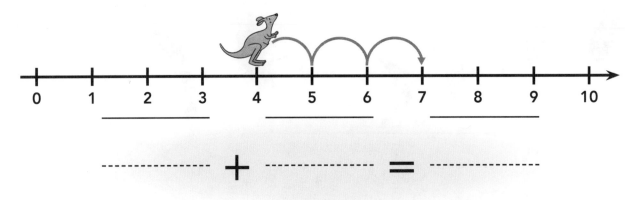

_____   _____   _____

- - - - - - - - - - - + - - - - - - - - - - = - - - - - - - - - - -

_____   _____   _____

Write the parts that make the whole.

2.
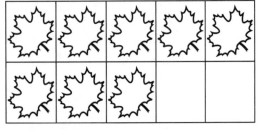

_____   _____

- - - - - - - - - - - + - - - - - - - - - - = 8

_____   _____

3.
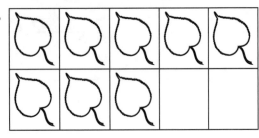

_____   _____

- - - - - - - - - - - + - - - - - - - - - - = 8

_____   _____

---

4. Write the answer.

$$5 + 4$$ $$3 + 3$$ $$5 + 2$$ $$4 + 1$$

- - - - - - - - -   - - - - - - - - -   - - - - - - - - -   - - - - - - - - -

_____   _____   _____   _____

Name _____

1. Fill in the blank.

How many in all?
_____

- - - - - - - - - - - - - -

_____

Draw and answer.

2.

_____

- - - - - - - - - -

3.

_____

- - - - - - - - - -

3 and 2 is _____. 1 and 3 is _____.

Write the addition fact.

4.

_____ + _____ = _____

5.

_____ + _____ = _____

1. Write the addition fact.

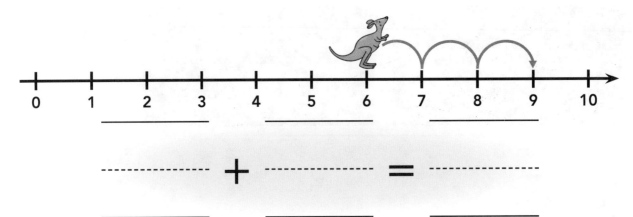

- - - - - - - - - - - - - - - + - - - - - - - - - - - - = - - - - - - - - - - - -

_____   _____   _____

Write in parts to make the whole.

2.

_____   _____

- - - - - - - - - - - - - + - - - - - - - - - - = 10

_____   _____

3.

_____   _____

- - - - - - - - - - - - - + - - - - - - - - - - = 10

_____   _____

4. Write the answer.

$$5 + 5$$ $$4 + 3$$ $$0 + 6$$ $$7 + 1$$

- - - - - - - -   - - - - - - - -   - - - - - - - -   - - - - - - - -

_____   _____   _____   _____

Chapter 12
Discover Subtraction

The sea is His, for He made it, and
His hands formed the dry land.
Psalm 95:5

Key Ideas:

Subtraction: subtracting from numbers up to 10

Subtraction: using a number line to subtract

Subtraction: using a ten-frame to subtract
numbers up to 10

Subtraction: using the "counting back" strategy
to subtract

There were 4 starfish. One washed away. How many are left?

MATH AT THE BEACH

$$4 - 1 = \underline{\hspace{2cm}}$$

Name _____

How many children are left? Circle the number.

1.

0 1 2

2.

1 2 3

3.

1 2 3

How many children are left? Circle the number.

1.

3 4 5

2.

3 4 5

3.

2 3 4

Count. Trace and write how many are left.

1.

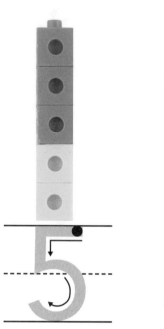

5

3

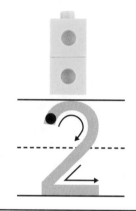

2

2.

_____   _____

_ _ _ _ _ _ _ _   _ _ _ _ _ _ _ _

_____   _____

How many are left?

_____

_ _ _ _ _ _ _ _

_____

3.

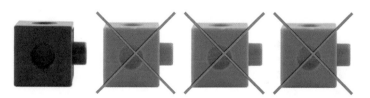

_____   _____

_ _ _ _ _ _ _ _   _ _ _ _ _ _ _ _

_____   _____

How many are left?

_____

_ _ _ _ _ _ _ _

_____

Count. Write the numbers.

1.

How many are left?

_____   _____   _____

-----------------   -----------------   -----------------

_____   _____   _____

2.

How many are left?

_____   _____   _____

-----------------   -----------------   -----------------

_____   _____   _____

3.

How many are left?

_____   _____   _____

-----------------   -----------------   -----------------

_____   _____   _____

4.

How many are left?

-----------------   -----------------   -----------------

_____   _____   _____

Draw a picture. Mark an X on the things that leave or are taken away. Write how many are left.

1.

_____

- - - - - - - - - - - - - - - -

3 take away 2 is _____.

2.

_____

- - - - - - - - - - - - - - - -

4 take away 2 is _____.

Draw a picture. Mark an **X** on the things that leave or are taken away. Write how many are left.

1.

2 take away 1 is _____.

2.

5 take away 3 is _____.

Mark Xs. Subtract.

1.

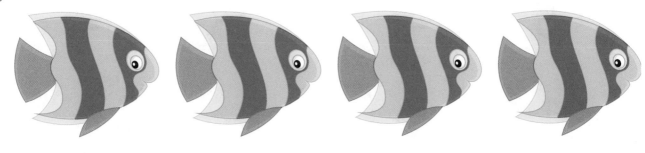

$$4 - 1 = \text{---------}$$

2.

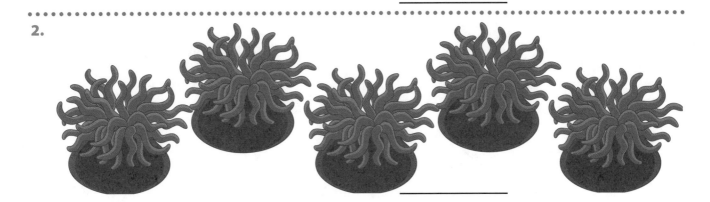

$$5 - 2 = \text{---------}$$

3.

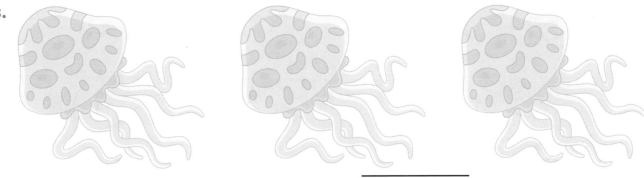

$$3 - 3 = \text{---------}$$

Subtract. Color the seashell with the correct answer.

1.
$$5 - 5 =$$
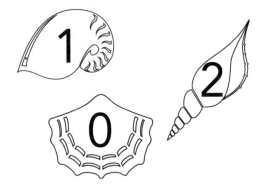

4.
$$3 - 2 =$$

2.
$$4 - 2 =$$

5.
$$1 - 0 =$$

3.
$$5 - 1 =$$

6.
$$4 - 3 =$$
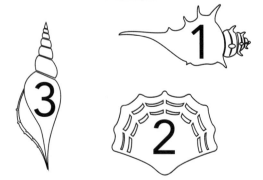

Name _____

Complete each subtraction problem.

1.

3

$-$ _____

‾‾‾‾‾‾‾‾‾‾

3.

_____

‾‾‾‾‾‾‾‾‾‾

$-$ _____

‾‾‾‾‾‾‾‾‾‾

2.

_____

$-$ _____

‾‾‾‾‾‾‾‾‾‾

4.

_____

$-$ _____

‾‾‾‾‾‾‾‾‾‾

Draw a path from each problem to the correct answer.

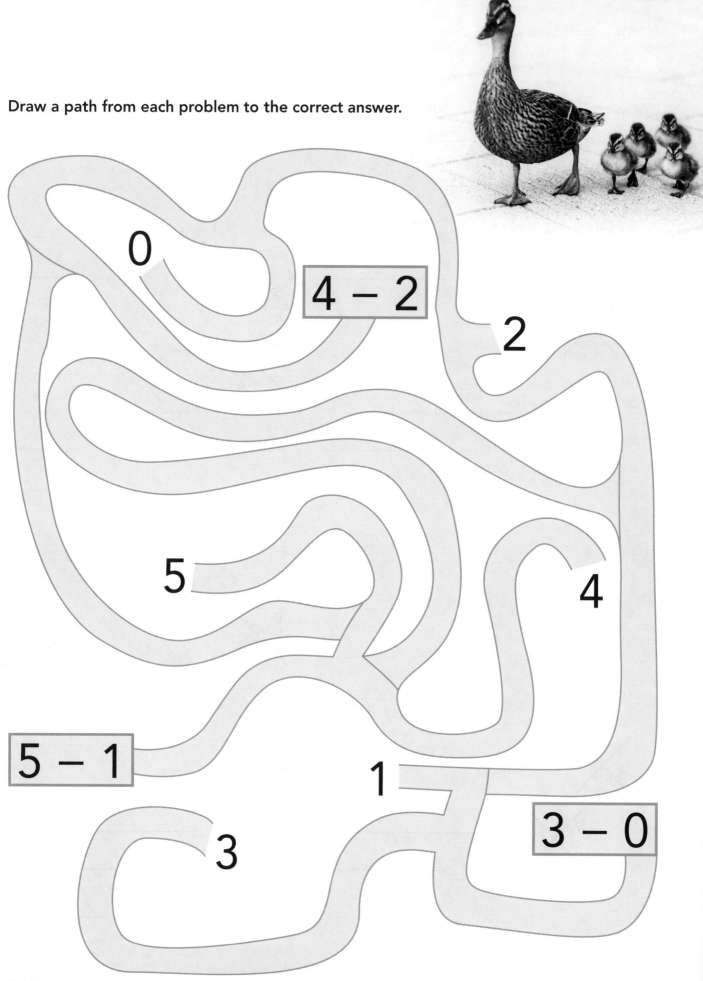

0

4 − 2

2

5

4

5 − 1

1

3 − 0

3

Name _____

Mark an **X** on any number of seashells. Write the numbers in the number sentences.

1.

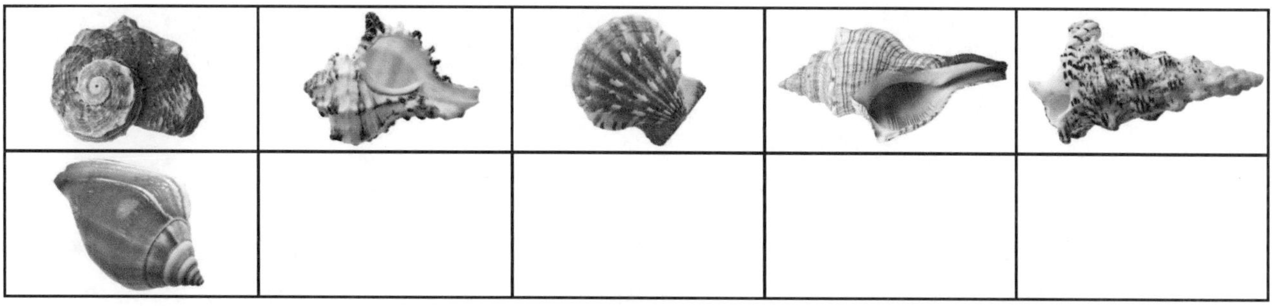

$$6 - \underline{} = \underline{}$$

2.

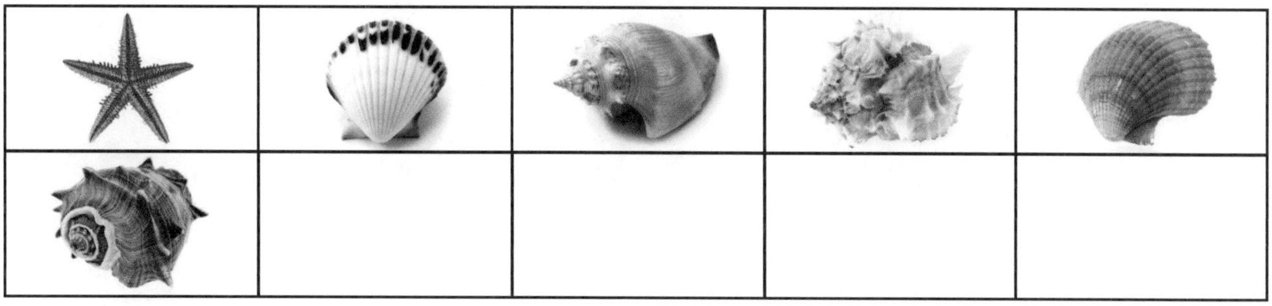

$$6 - \underline{} = \underline{}$$

3.

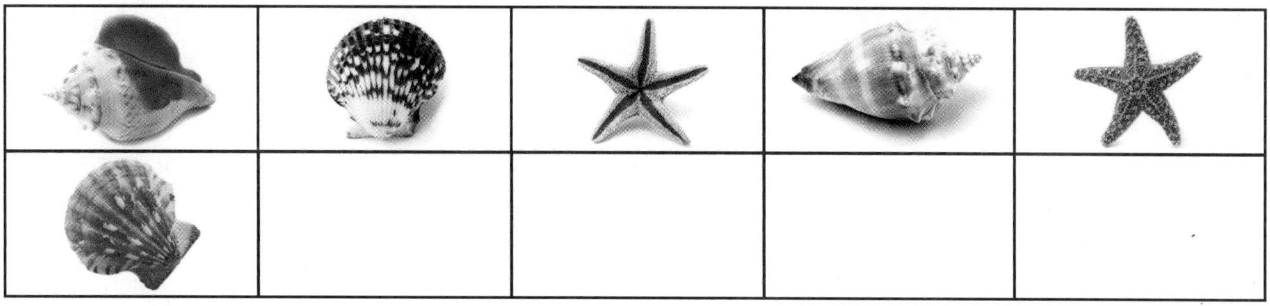

$$6 - \underline{} = \underline{}$$

Circle two beach items that equal the number on the left.

1.

2

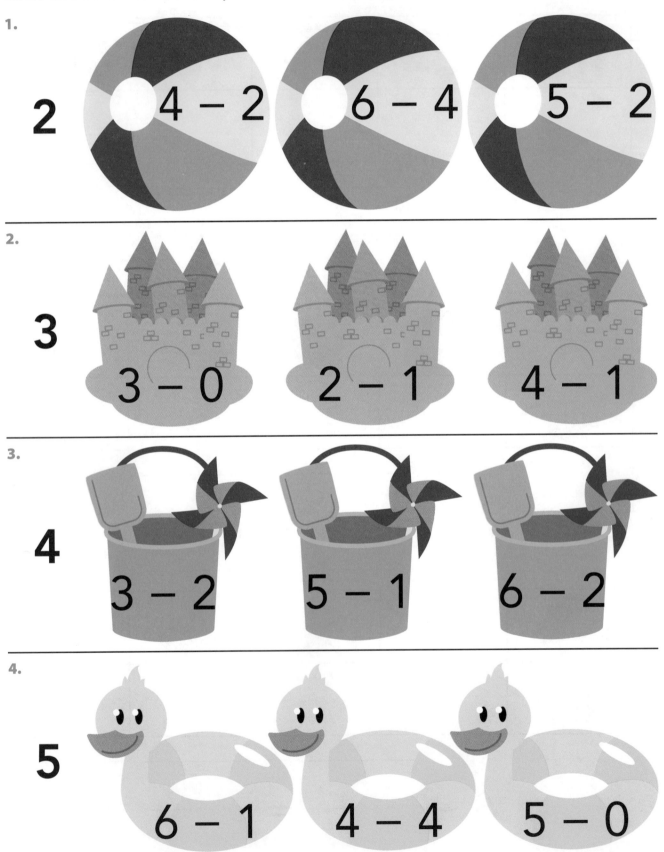

4 – 2   6 – 4   5 – 2

2.

3

3 – 0   2 – 1   4 – 1

3.

4

3 – 2   5 – 1   6 – 2

4.

5

6 – 1   4 – 4   5 – 0

Name _____

Draw a picture of the story. Mark **X**s. Write the number sentence.

1.

_____   _____   _____

- - - - - - - - - - **—** - - - - - - - - - - **=** - - - - - - - - - -

_____   _____   _____

2.

_____   _____   _____

- - - - - - - - - - **—** - - - - - - - - - - **=** - - - - - - - - - -

_____   _____   _____

Draw a picture of the story. Mark Xs. Write the number sentence.

1.

_____   _____   _____

- - - - - - - - - - - - -   **—**   - - - - - - - - - - - -   **=**   - - - - - - - - - - - -

_____   _____   _____

2.

_____   _____   _____

- - - - - - - - - - - - -   **—**   - - - - - - - - - - - -   **=**   - - - - - - - - - - - -

_____   _____   _____

Name _____

Write each number sentence.

1.

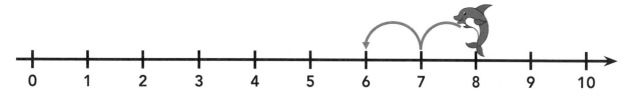

start	count back	stop

- - - - - - - - - - — - - - - - - - - - = - - - - - - - - -

_____   _____   _____

2.

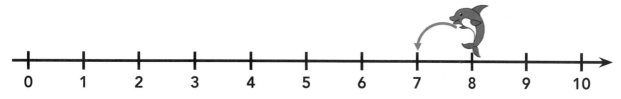

start	count back	stop

- - - - - - - - - - — - - - - - - - - - = - - - - - - - - -

_____   _____   _____

3.

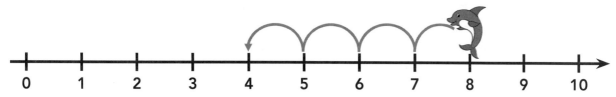

start	count back	stop

- - - - - - - - - - — - - - - - - - - - = - - - - - - - - -

_____   _____   _____

© *Mathematics* Kindergarten

Circle the correct number sentence.

1.

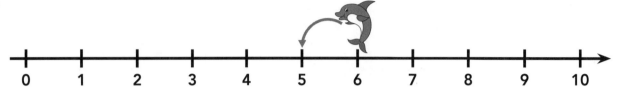

$6 - 3 = 3$ $6 - 1 = 5$

2.

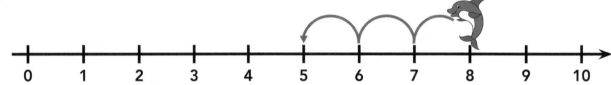

$8 - 3 = 5$ $8 - 5 = 3$

3.

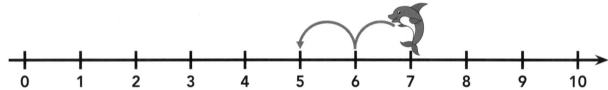

$7 - 5 = 2$ $7 - 2 = 5$

4.

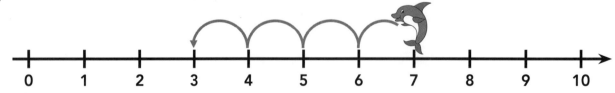

$7 - 4 = 3$ $7 - 2 = 5$

Name _____

Estimate how many are left. Write the subtraction fact.

1.

Estimate.

_____

- - - - - - - - - - - - - - -

_____

_____   _____

─ ─ ─ 7 ─ ─   —   - - - - - - - - - - - - -   =   - - - - - - - - - - - - -

_____   _____   _____

2.

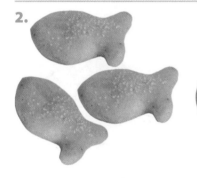

Estimate.

_____

- - - - - - - - - - - - - - -

_____

_____   _____

─ ─ 8 ─ ─   —   - - - - - - - - - - - - -   =   - - - - - - - - - - - - -

_____   _____   _____

3.

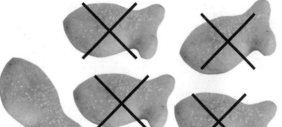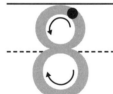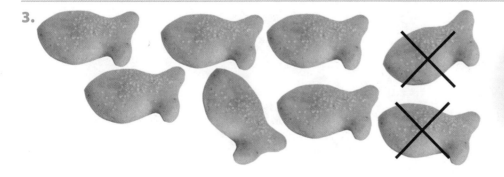

Estimate.

_____

- - - - - - - - - - - - - - -

_____

_____   _____

─ ─ 8 ─ ─   —   - - - - - - - - - - - - -   =   - - - - - - - - - - - - -

_____   _____   _____

Estimate how many are left. Write the subtraction fact.

1.

Estimate.
_____
- - - - - - - - - - - - -
_____

___9___ - _____ = _____

2.

Estimate.
_____
- - - - - - - - - - - - -
_____

___9___ - _____ = _____

3.

Estimate.
_____
- - - - - - - - - - - - -
_____

___9___ - _____ = _____

Name _____

Cut. Count and glue on the missing part.

1. 10

_____

7

2. 10

_____

3

3. 10

_____

5

4. 10

_____

4

✂ -

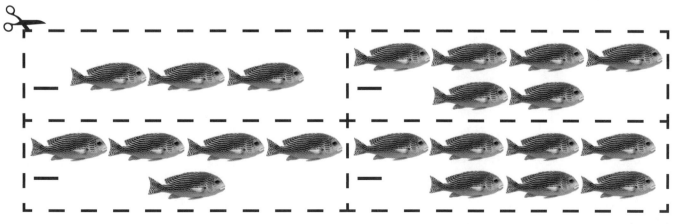

Draw in the missing part. Write the missing number.

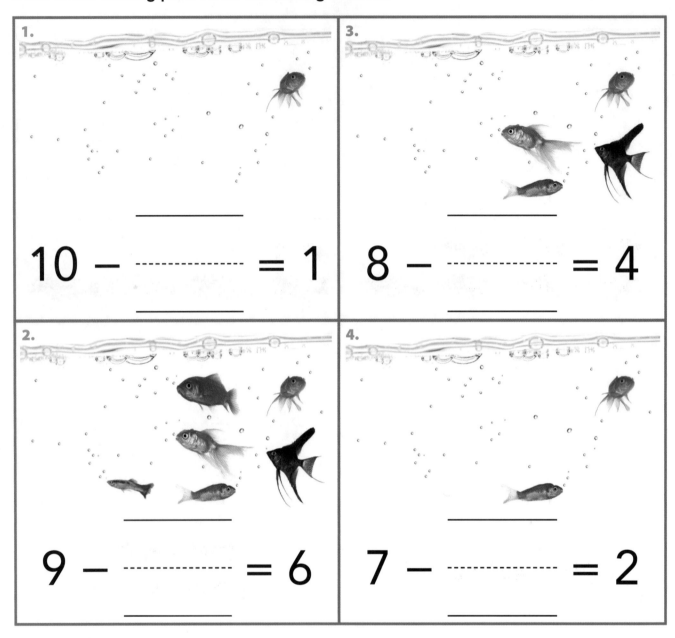

1.

_____

$10 - \text{------} = 1$

_____

2.

_____

$9 - \text{------} = 6$

_____

3.

_____

$8 - \text{------} = 4$

_____

4.

_____

$7 - \text{------} = 2$

_____

Name _____

Read the graph. Color in the circles to answer the questions.

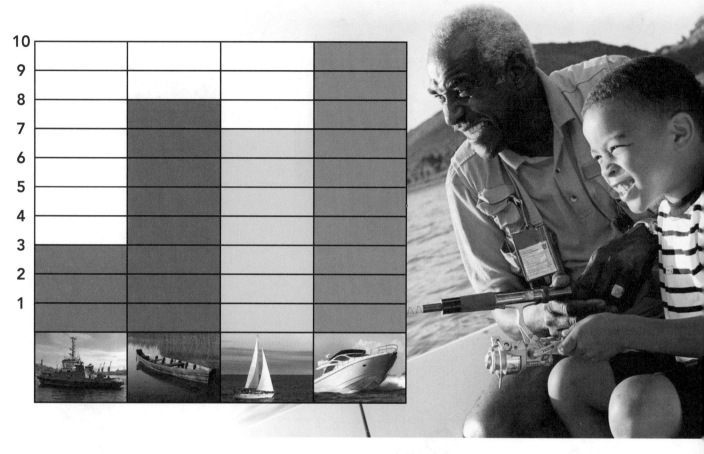

1. Which is the greatest number of boats?

2. Which is the fewest number of boats?

3. How many more  than  ?

 5   ◯ 8   ◯ 7

Read the graph. Write the numbers and subtract.

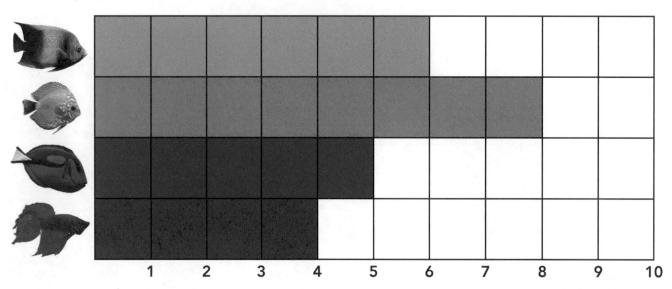

1. _____ _____ _____

   - - - - - - - - - — - - - - - - - = - - - - - - -

   _____ _____ _____

2. _____ _____ _____

   - - - - - - - - - — - - - - - - - = - - - - - - -

   _____ _____ _____

3. _____ _____ _____

   - - - - - - - - - — - - - - - - - = - - - - - - -

   _____ _____

Name _____

Draw a picture. Mark Xs. Write how many are left.

1.

5 take away 3 is _____.

2.

4 take away 1 is _____.

Mark Xs. Subtract.

3.

7 − 2 = _____

4.

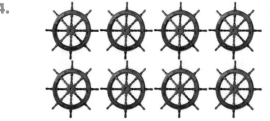

8 − 4 = _____

5. Write the number sentence.

_____ − _____ = _____

Mark an X on any part. Write the number sentence.

1.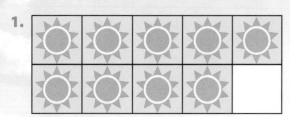

$9 -$ _____ $=$ _____

2.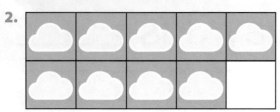

$9 -$ _____ $=$ _____

---

3. Write the number sentence.

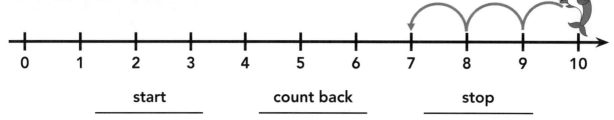

start   count back   stop
_____   _____   _____

_____ $-$ _____ $=$ _____

_____   _____   _____

---

4. Subtract.

$$7 - 3 = \text{_____}$$

$$9 - 6 = \text{_____}$$

$$8 - 2 = \text{_____}$$

$$6 - 1 = \text{_____}$$

$5 - 4 =$ _____

Name _____

Draw a picture. Mark Xs. Write how many are left.

1.

5 take away 4 is _____ .

2.

4 take away 2 is _____ .

Mark Xs. Subtract.

3.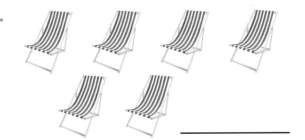

6 − 3 = _____

4.

7 − 4 = _____

5. Write the number sentence.

_____ _____ _____

_____ − _____ = _____

_____ _____ _____

Mark Xs. Write the number sentence.

1.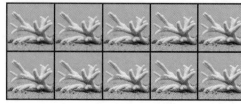

$$10 - \underline{\hspace{3cm}} = \underline{\hspace{2cm}}$$

2.

$$10 - \underline{\hspace{3cm}} = \underline{\hspace{2cm}}$$

3. Write the number sentence.

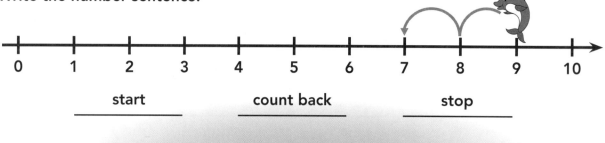

| 0   1   2   3   4   5   6   7   8   9   10 |

start   count back   stop

$$\underline{\hspace{3cm}} - \underline{\hspace{3cm}} = \underline{\hspace{3cm}}$$

4. Subtract.

$$\begin{array}{r} 7 \\ -\ 0 \\ \hline \end{array} \qquad \begin{array}{r} 8 \\ -\ 6 \\ \hline \end{array} \qquad \begin{array}{r} 6 \\ -\ 5 \\ \hline \end{array} \qquad \begin{array}{r} 10 \\ -\ 4 \\ \hline \end{array}$$

$$5 - 2 = \underline{\hspace{3cm}}$$

Chapter 13
Measurement

The Lord will guide you always....
You will be like a well-watered garden.
Isaiah 58:11

Key Ideas:

Measurement: comparing the lengths of everyday objects

Measurement: comparing the volume of everyday objects

Measurement: comparing the weight of everyday objects to one pound

Measurement: estimating, measuring, and recording temperature using a thermometer

Write how long each item is. Circle the longest item. Mark an X on the shortest item.

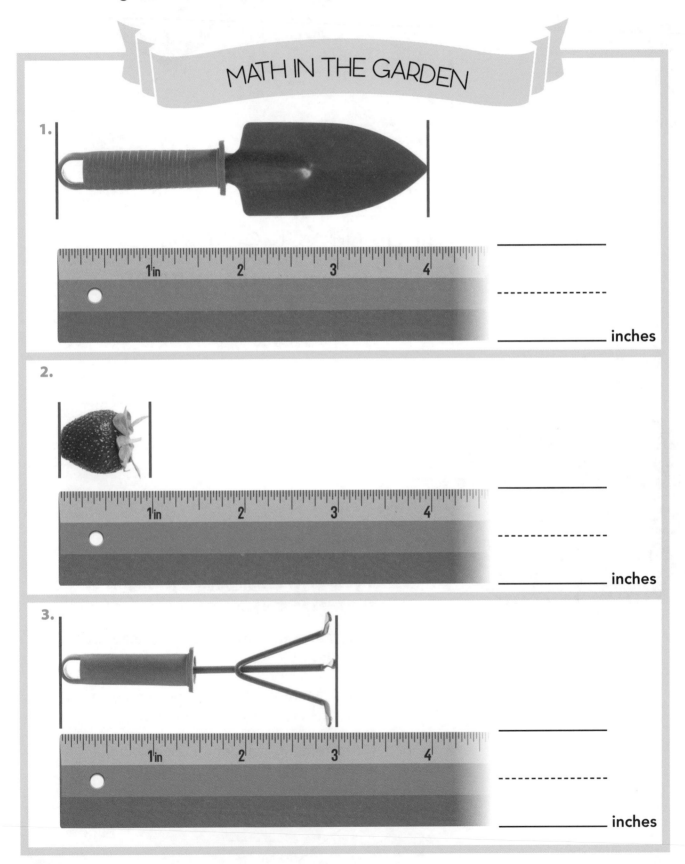

MATH IN THE GARDEN

1.

_____
- - - - - - - - - - - - - - -
_____ inches

2.

_____
- - - - - - - - - - - - - - -
_____ inches

3.

_____
- - - - - - - - - - - - - - -
_____ inches

Name _____

Count how many cubes long. Write.

1.

_____

- - - - - - - - - - - - - -

_____

2.

_____

- - - - - - - - - - - - - -

_____

3.

_____

- - - - - - - - - - - - - -

_____

4.

_____

- - - - - - - - - - - - - -

_____

Estimate how many cubes tall. Measure and count.

1.

Estimate. _____

- - - - - - - - - - - - - - - -

_____

Count. _____

- - - - - - - - - - - - - - - -

_____

3.

Estimate. _____

- - - - - - - - - - - - - - - -

_____

Count. _____

- - - - - - - - - - - - - - - -

_____

2.

Estimate. _____

- - - - - - - - - - - - - - - -

_____

Count. _____

- - - - - - - - - - - - - - - -

_____

4.

Estimate. _____

- - - - - - - - - - - - - - - -

_____

Count. _____

- - - - - - - - - - - - - - - -

_____

Name _____

Which is longer? Circle.

1.

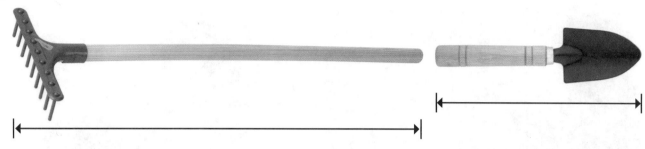

2.

3.

4. Draw a shorter insect.

5. Draw a longer insect.

Who is shorter? Circle.

1.

2.

3. Draw a shorter tree.

4. Draw a taller tree.

Name _____

Number the pictures 1, 2, and 3 from shortest to longest.

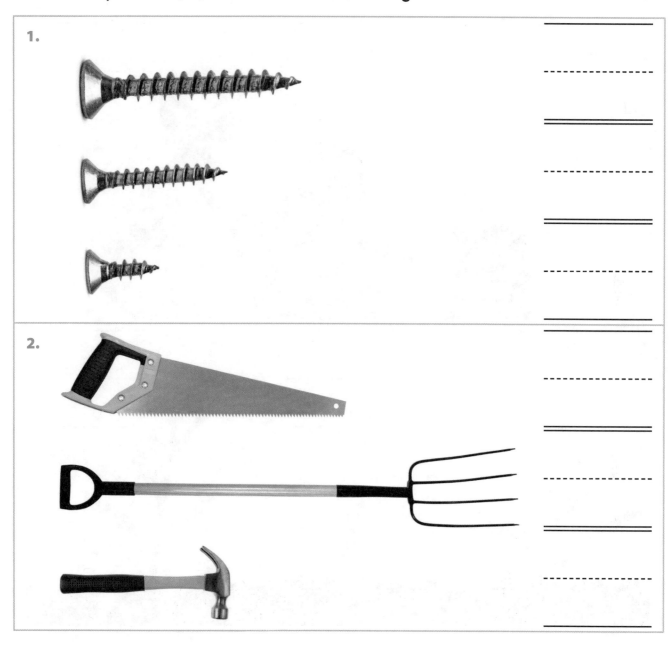

1.

2.

3. Draw longer and longest.

Number the pictures 1, 2, **and** 3 **from shortest to tallest.**

1.

--------------- --------------- ---------------

2.

--------------- --------------- ---------------

3. **Draw shortest and tallest.**

Name _____

Circle the best way to measure each real-life object.

1.

inches feet

2.

inches feet

4.
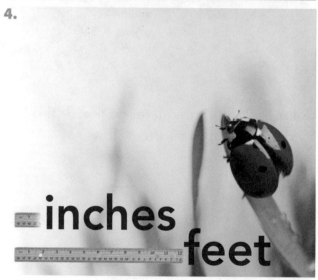
inches feet

3.

inches feet

5.

inches feet

Color the number squares to match the heights of the flowers. Circle the tallest flower.
Mark an X on the shortest flower.

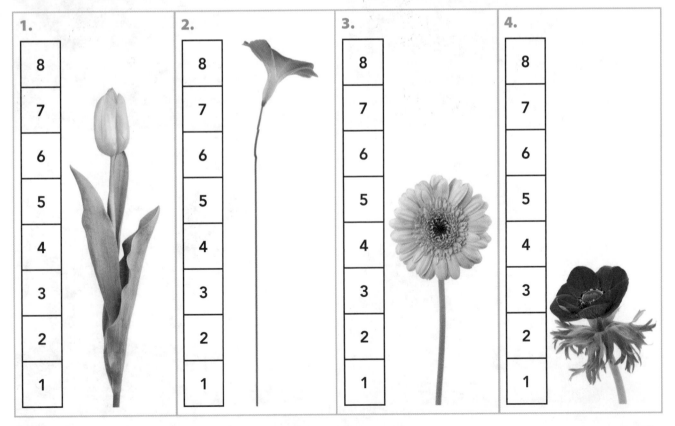

1.

| 8 |
| 7 |
| 6 |
| 5 |
| 4 |
| 3 |
| 2 |
| 1 |

2.

| 8 |
| 7 |
| 6 |
| 5 |
| 4 |
| 3 |
| 2 |
| 1 |

3.

| 8 |
| 7 |
| 6 |
| 5 |
| 4 |
| 3 |
| 2 |
| 1 |

4.

| 8 |
| 7 |
| 6 |
| 5 |
| 4 |
| 3 |
| 2 |
| 1 |

Name _____

Use a ruler to measure each strip.
Write how many inches.

1.

_____

- - - - - - - - - - - - - - -

_____ inches

2.

_____

- - - - - - - - - - - - - - -

_____ inches

3.

_____

- - - - - - - - - - - - - - -

_____ inches

4.

_____

- - - - - - - - - - - - - - -

_____ inches

5.

_____

- - - - - - - - - - - - - - -

_____ inches

Use a ruler to measure each object. Write how many inches.

1.

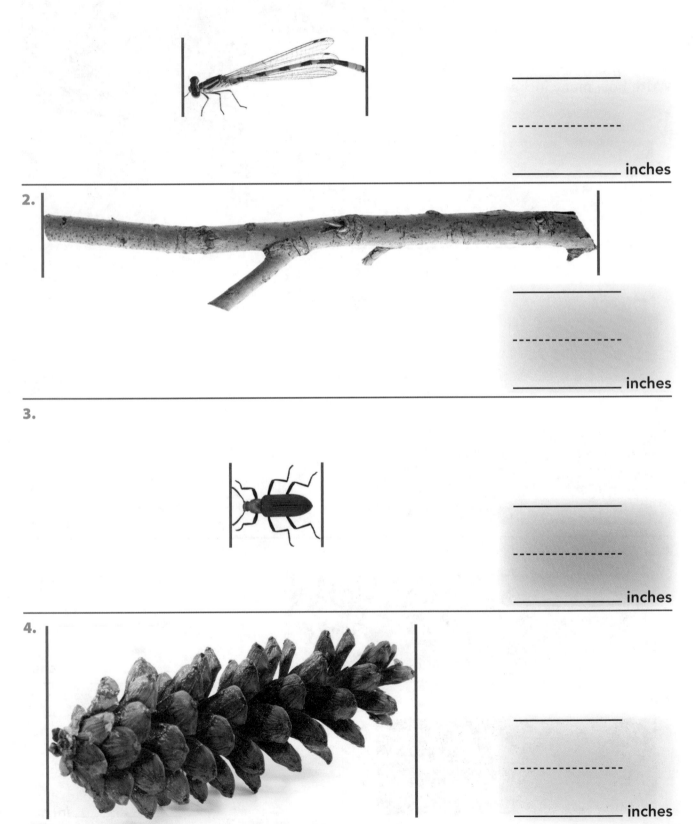

_____

- - - - - - - - - - - - - - - -

_____ inches

2.

_____

- - - - - - - - - - - - - - - -

_____ inches

3.

_____

- - - - - - - - - - - - - - - -

_____ inches

4.

_____

- - - - - - - - - - - - - - - -

_____ inches

Name _____

Mark an **X** on the item that holds more.

1.

4.

2.

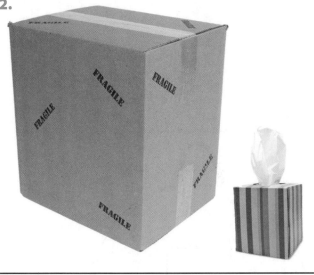

5.

3.

6.

Color red the item that holds less.

1.

3.

2.

4.

Name _____

Which holds about a cup? Circle.

1.

2.

3.

4.

Number the items from 1 to 3. Number from least to most.

1.

——————— ——————— ———————

---------------- ---------------- ----------------

——————— ——————— ———————

2.

——————— ——————— ———————

---------------- ---------------- ----------------

——————— ——————— ———————

3.

——————— ——————— ———————

---------------- ---------------- ----------------

——————— ——————— ———————

Cut. Glue on the correct side of the scale.

light

heavy

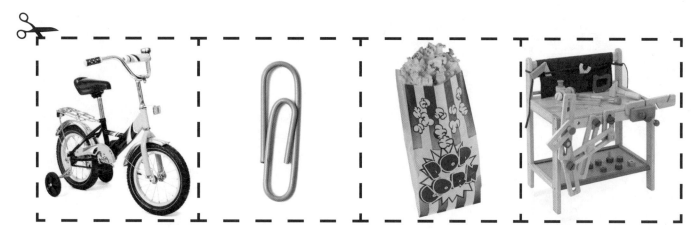

Circle the lighter object. Draw a line under the heavier object.

1.

3.

2.

4.

Name _____

1. Mark an X on each item that weighs just ounces.

2. Mark an X on each item that weighs pounds.

© *Mathematics* Kindergarten

Circle the correct weight of each item.

ounces | pounds

1.

2

20

4.

10

100

2.

2

12

5.

20

100

3.

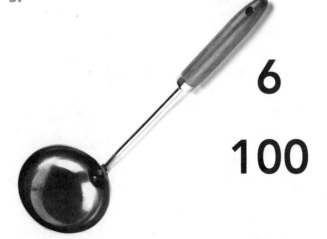

6

100

6.

5

50

Name _____

Circle the item that is hot. Draw a line under the item that is cold.

1.

4.

2.

5.

3.

6.

Color the thermometer to show the temperature. Draw an activity you would do outdoors at that temperature.

1. # 70°F

2. # 30°F

100		
90	hot day	
80		
70	warm day	
60		
50	cool day	
40		
30	cold day	
20		
10		
0		
−10		

100		
90	hot day	
80		
70	warm day	
60		
50	cool day	
40		
30	cold day	
20		
10		
0		
−10		

Name _____

Cut and glue each picture under the correct thermometer. Circle the coldest thermometer. Mark an X on the hottest thermometer.

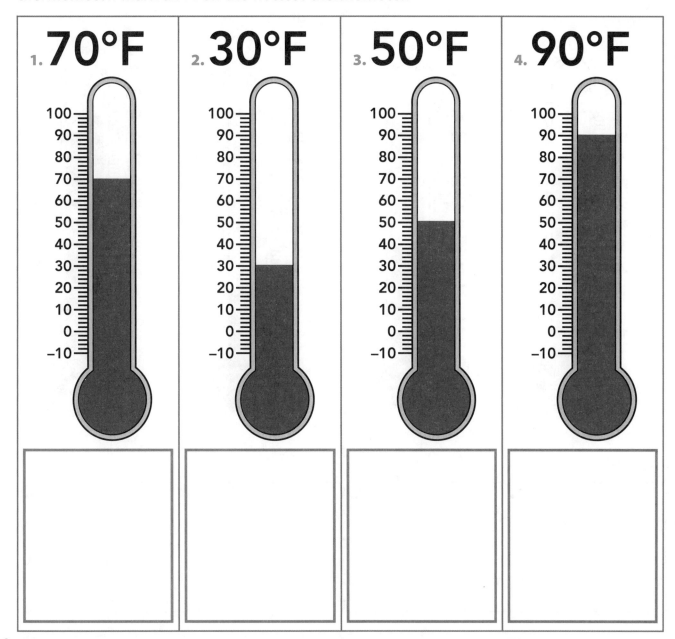

Write the temperature. Circle the correct thermometer in each set.

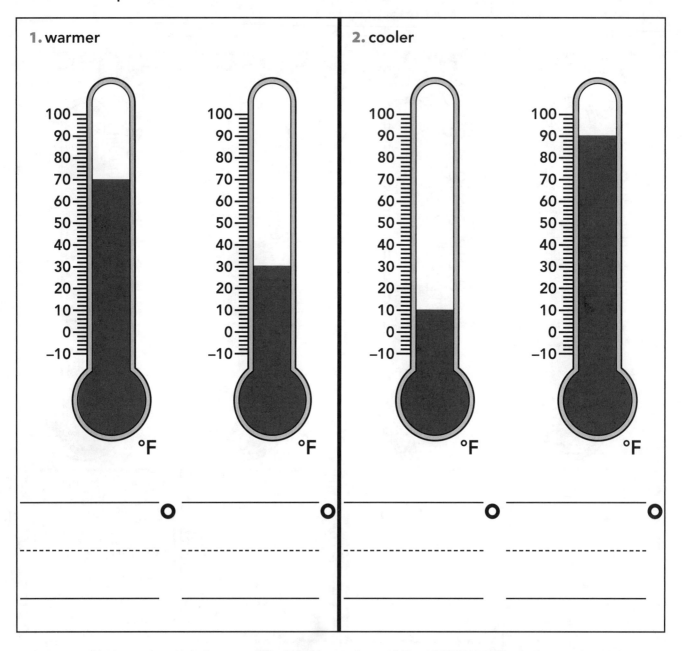

1. warmer

2. cooler

Name _____

Listen and color the graph.

How Tall Is He?

5				
4				
3				
2				
1				
	3-month-old baby boy (2 feet)	3-year-old boy (3 feet)	7-year-old boy (4 feet)	13-year-old boy (5 feet)

Listen and color the graph.

How Tall Is the Bamboo Plant?

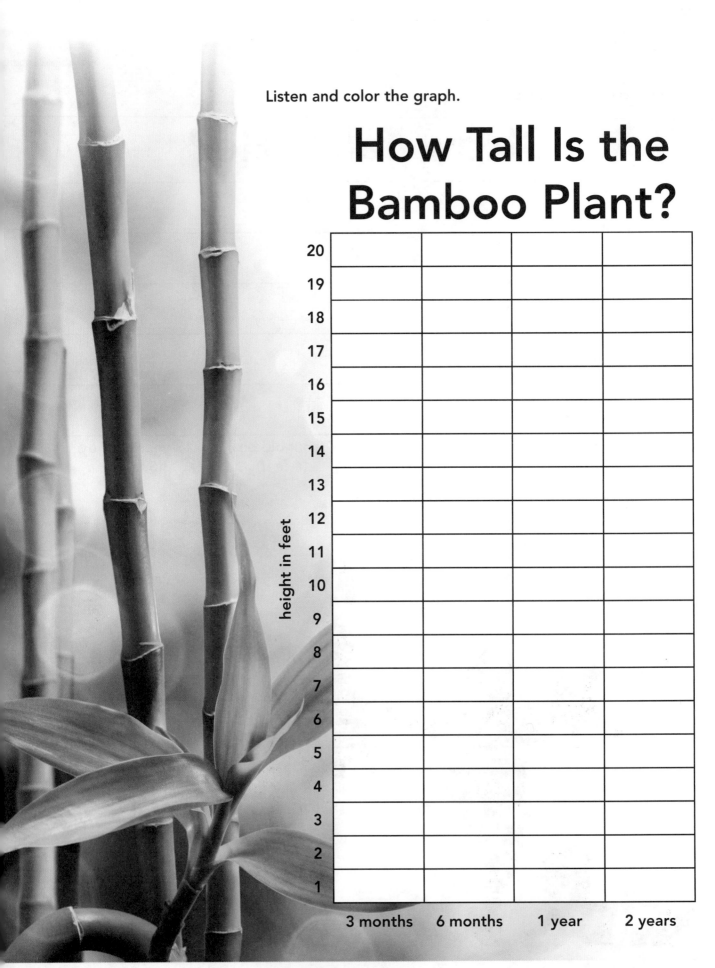

height in feet

	3 months	6 months	1 year	2 years

Name _____

Circle the correct object.

1. shorter

3. holds more

2. longer

4. holds less

5. Measure and write the length.

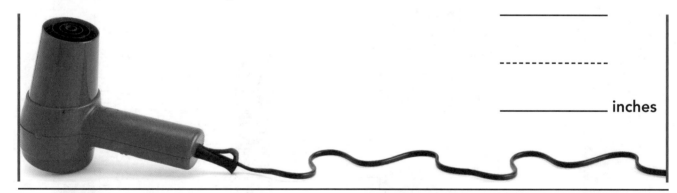

_____

- - - - - - - - - - - - - - - -

_____ inches

6. Listen and mark.

Circle the correct object.

1. heavier

2. lighter

3. ounces

4. pounds

---

5. Fill in the circle to match the temperature.

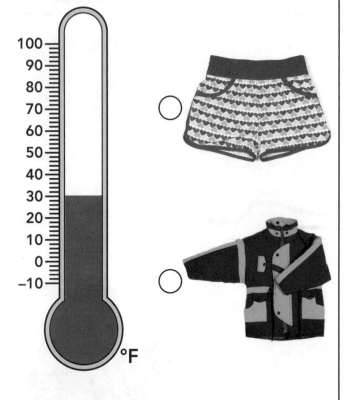

6. Write the temperature. Circle the warmer thermometer.

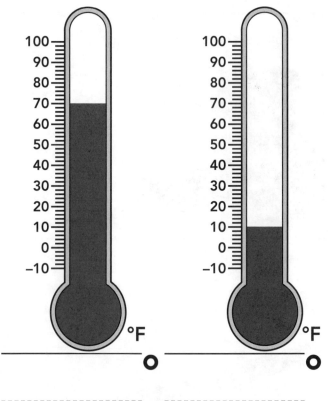

Circle the correct object.

1. shorter

4. taller

2. longer

5. holds more

3. shorter

6. holds less

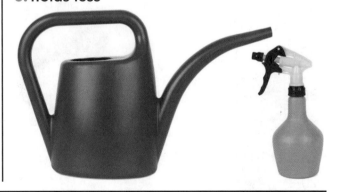

7. Measure and write the length.

- - - - - - - - - - - - - - -

_____ inches

Circle the correct object.

1. heavier

2. lighter

3. ounces

4. pounds

5. Fill in the circle to match the temperature.

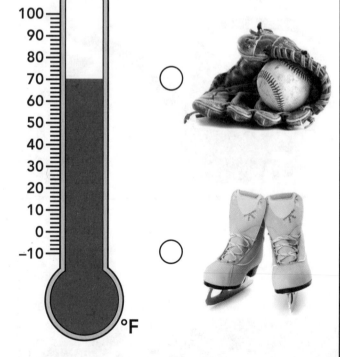

6. Write the temperature. Circle the cooler thermometer.

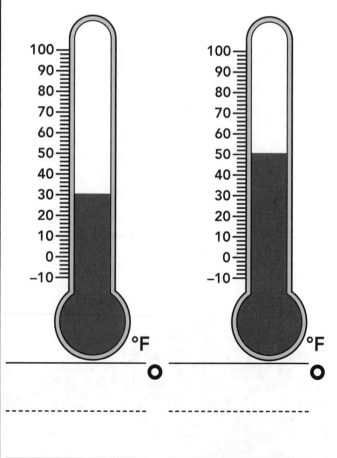

°F ○

°F ○

----

1. Color the teacup on bottom.

2. Color two ways to make 5.

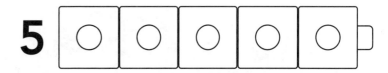

3. Color to finish the pattern.

4. Color to match the shapes.

cone   sphere   cube   cylinder

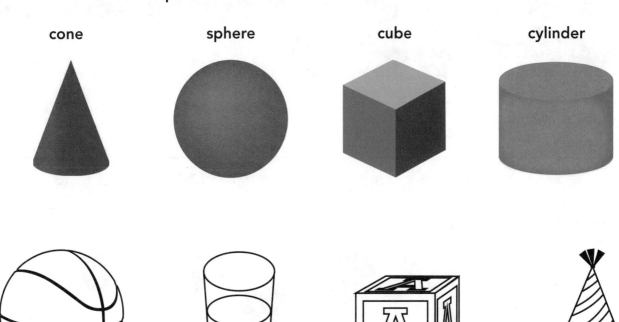

1. Circle second.

2. Circle a tool that measures length.

3. Circle how many balls.

26

16

15

4. Circle skip counting by 2s.

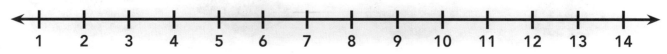

5. Sort the buttons. Circle groups that are the same.

Name _____

1. Draw the hour hand for 9:00.

2. Draw to make the sets the same number.

3. Draw the other half.

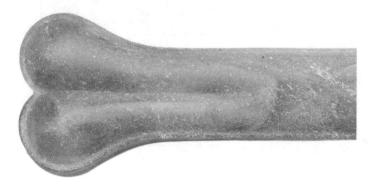

© *Mathematics* Kindergarten

1. Write the amount.

_____

- - - - - - - - - - - - - -

_____ ¢

Add. Write the answers.

2.
$$2$$
$$+\ 3$$
- - - - - - - - - -

_____

3.
$$1$$
$$+\ 6$$
- - - - - - - - - -

_____

Subtract. Write the answers.

4.

$$7 - 3 =$$

_____

- - - - - - - - - -

_____

5.

$$8 - 2 =$$

_____

- - - - - - - - - -

_____

---

6. Count. Write the number.

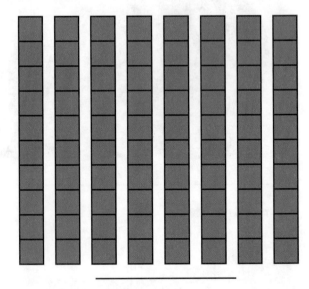

_____

- - - - - - - - - - - - - -

_____